The Open University

M249 Pr statistics

Book 4

Bayesian statistics

About this course

M249 Practical Modern Statistics uses the software packages *SPSS for Windows* (SPSS Inc.) and *WinBUGS*, and other software. This software is provided as part of the course, and its use is covered in the *Introduction to statistical modelling* and in the four computer books associated with *Books 1* to *4*.

Cover image courtesy of NASA. This photograph, acquired by the ASTER instrument on NASA's Terra satellite, shows an aerial view of a large alluvial fan between the Kunlun and Altun mountains in China's Xinjiang province. For more information, see NASA's Earth Observatory website at http://earthobservatory.nasa.gov.

This publication forms part of an Open University course. Details of this and other Open University courses can be obtained from the Student Registration and Enquiry Service, The Open University, PO Box 197, Milton Keynes, MK7 6BJ, United Kingdom: tel. +44 (0)870 300 6090, e-mail general-enquiries@open.ac.uk

Alternatively, you may visit the Open University website at http://www.open.ac.uk where you can learn more about the wide range of courses and packs offered at all levels by The Open University.

To purchase a selection of Open University course materials, visit http://www.ouw.co.uk, or contact Open University Worldwide, Michael Young Building, Walton Hall, Milton Keynes, MK7 6AA, United Kingdom, for a brochure: tel. +44 (0)1908 858793, fax +44 (0)1908 858787, e-mail ouw-customer-services@open.ac.uk

The Open University, Walton Hall, Milton Keynes, MK7 6AA.

First published 2007.

Edited, designed and typeset by The Open University, using the Open University TEX System.

Printed and bound in the United Kingdom by Charlesworth Press, Wakefield.

ISBN 978 0 7492 1369 5

1.1

Contents

Study guide

You should schedule 20 study sessions for this book. This includes time for working through *Computer Book 4*, answering the TMA questions and consolidating your work on this book. You should schedule four study sessions for Part I, six for Part II, five for Part III and five for Part IV.

The sections vary in length. In Part I, Section 1 is very short. In Part II, Section 7 is shorter than average and Section 8 is longer than average. In Part III, Sections 10, 11, 13 and 15 are all shorter than average, and Section 12 is longer than average. In Part IV, Section 17 is shorter than average, and Section 19 is longer than average.

As you study this book, you will be asked to work through the chapters of *Computer Book 4*. We recommend that you work through them at the points indicated in the text. The software package *LearnBayes* is introduced in Section 4, and the software package WinBUGS in Section 12.

One possible study pattern is as follows.

Part I

Study session 1: Sections 1 and 2.
Study session 2: Section 3.
Study session 3: Section 4. You will need access to your computer for this session.
Study session 4: TMA questions on Part I.

Part II

Study session 5: Section 5.
Study session 6: Section 6.
Study session 7: Section 7. You will need access to your computer for this session.
Study session 8: Section 8. You will need access to your computer for this session.
Study session 9: Section 9. You will need access to your computer for this session.
Study session 10: TMA questions on Part II.

Part III

Study session 11: Sections 10 and 11.
Study session 12: Section 12. You will need access to your computer for this session.
Study session 13: Sections 13 and 14.
Study session 14: Section 15. You will need access to your computer for this session.
Study session 15: TMA questions on Part III.

Part IV

Study session 16: Section 16. You will need access to your computer for this session.
Study session 17: Section 17.
Study session 18: Section 18. You will need access to your computer for this session.
Study session 19: Section 19. You will need access to your computer for this session.
Study session 20: TMA questions on Part IV, and consolidation of your work on this book.

If you follow this study pattern, then Study sessions 1, 8, 12 and 13 may be long ones, and Study sessions 7, 9, 14 and 17 are likely to be shorter than average.

Introduction

This book provides an introduction to an area of statistics known as Bayesian statistics. The name 'Bayesian' refers to the Reverend Thomas Bayes, an English 18th century Presbyterian minister and amateur mathematician and scientist.

In the early 18th century, probability theory was being developed to answer questions concerning gambling and insurance. Mathematicians of the time knew how to calculate the probability of certain events, given specified conditions. For example, they could solve the following problem. Given that there are n red balls and m black balls in a bag, what is the probability of selecting a black ball? However, they did not know how to tackle the inverse of this problem: given that a black ball has been selected, what is the probability that there are n red balls and m black balls in the bag? Bayes' solution to this problem involved using a general result which has become known as Bayes' theorem. This theorem, which was published in 1763 (after Bayes' death), underlies the Bayesian approach to statistics.

Thomas Bayes (1702–1761)

You may be wondering why Bayesian statistics is in a course on 'modern statistics' when Bayes' theorem itself is so old. The reason is that although Bayes' method was taken up enthusiastically by probabilists of the time, it was challenged in the 19th century because it uses what are known as 'prior probabilities'. In the first half of the 20th century, a completely different statistical theory was developed, now called 'classical' or 'frequentist' statistics. This is the approach to statistics with which you will be familiar, and is the approach used elsewhere in M249. The modern Bayesian movement began in the second half of the 20th century. Bayesian statistics was, however, very difficult to implement until powerful computers became widely available and new computational techniques were developed in the late 1980s and early 1990s. Since then, Bayesian methods have become extremely popular and have been used in many diverse areas including medicine, criminal justice and internet search engines.

You will learn about prior probabilities in Part I.

Whereas in classical statistics the data alone are used to learn about unknown parameters and quantities, in Bayesian statistics any relevant information external to the data is also used. To illustrate the Bayesian and classical approaches, consider the following statistical problem. In November 1989, the ten publicly-owned water authorities in England and Wales were privatized. One of the (many) requirements of water authorities prior to privatization was to estimate the cost of maintaining, replacing or improving their underground water pipes, sewers and associated structures. The authorities could not know the condition of these pipes definitely without physically digging them up, and with millions of kilometres of underground pipes this obviously was not an option. Several of the authorities proposed dividing their region into zones, sampling a number of these zones randomly, estimating the cost of maintaining, replacing and improving the pipes in each sampled zone, and then using these zone estimates to estimate the total cost for their region. For each zone, obtaining a single observation could be very costly, so data were not abundant. However, the authorities did have a lot of other information available, so they had a good idea of how their pipes performed generally. For example, they knew which zones were more costly than others, and so on. This information can be used in addition to the data when using a Bayesian approach to estimate the total cost, whereas a classical approach can use only the data.

O'Hagan, A. (1997) The ABLE story: Bayesian asset management in the water industry. In French, S. and Smith, J.Q. (eds) *The Practice of Bayesian Analysis*. Arnold, London, pp. 173–198.

Even when no extra information is available, the Bayesian approach is sometimes preferred to a classical approach. There are two main reasons for this. First, the Bayesian approach is quite general and can be used for problems of arbitrary complexity, many of which cannot be handled by classical statistics. Secondly, the results from the Bayesian approach are easy to interpret, by both statisticians and non-statisticians.

As already mentioned, in Bayesian statistics there are two sources of information regarding the unknown parameter or quantity — information external to the data, and the data themselves. The two sources of information are combined using Bayes' theorem, then inferences about the unknown parameter, or other quantity of interest, are made. In Part I, some of the ideas which underpin Bayesian statistics are discussed, and a framework for Bayesian inference is introduced. In Part II, some Bayesian models, called conjugate models, are described. These models are simple to use, and are ideal to illustrate the basic ideas of Bayesian inference.

However, Bayesian statistics can be computationally difficult in practice. In Part III, a technique called simulation which can simplify the computations is introduced. A particular method of simulation called Markov chain Monte Carlo simulation, or MCMC for short, is explored in Part IV. MCMC is a powerful tool for Bayesian analysis and is the principal reason why Bayesian statistics became computationally feasible in the late 20th century.

Part I   The Bayesian approach

Introduction to Part I

One of the key ideas in Bayesian statistics is that knowledge about anything unknown can be expressed probabilistically. For example, suppose we are interested in the proposition E, where

E = a major earthquake will occur in Europe in the next ten years.

A proposition is any kind of statement which can be true or false.

Since E is unobserved, there is uncertainty as to whether or not E is true. In Bayesian statistics, knowledge about E can be expressed by $P(E)$, the probability that E is true. The closer the value of $P(E)$ is to 1, the more likely E is to be true, and the closer $P(E)$ is to 0, the more likely E is to be false. In a Bayesian statistical analysis, probabilities such as $P(E)$, which represent knowledge about E, need to be estimated. How this might be done is the focus of Section 1.

Suppose that data are observed, or new information becomes available, to help learn about a proposition. The data (or information) will update the knowledge about the proposition. This updated knowledge can be expressed probabilistically. In Section 2, Bayes' theorem is introduced. This provides a method of calculating the probability representing the updated knowledge.

In most statistical problems, it is not simply the probability of a proposition that is of interest, but the more general problem of learning about an unknown parameter or, indeed, any unobserved quantity. In Bayesian statistics, knowledge about an unknown parameter, or quantity, can also be expressed probabilistically. Bayes' theorem provides a method of calculating the updated knowledge about the unknown parameter or quantity, as represented probabilistically, after observing any relevant data or information. How this can be done is discussed in Section 3, and a framework for Bayesian inference is established. In Section 4, you will use the software package *LearnBayes* to explore the ideas introduced in Part I, and to develop your understanding of these ideas.

1   Estimating probabilities

Often in Bayesian statistics the probability of some proposition has to be estimated. In this section, several ways in which this might be done are discussed. These include simply calculating probabilities and using relative frequencies to estimate probabilities. You will be familiar with these methods from classical statistics. Probabilities that cannot be estimated objectively and need to be estimated subjectively are also considered.

Calculating probabilities

Some probabilities can simply be calculated, as illustrated in Example 1.1.

Example 1.1   Tossing a coin

If a coin is tossed, then assuming that the coin is fair, the probability that it lands heads up is calculated as
$$P(\text{head}) = \frac{\text{number of ways of getting a head}}{\text{number of possible outcomes (head or tail)}} = \frac{1}{2}. \quad \blacklozenge$$

Activity 1.1   Rolling a die

A fair die with faces numbered from 1 to 6 is rolled. Calculate the probability that the die lands with an even number uppermost.

In Example 1.1 and Activity 1.1, there is little uncertainty about the values of the probabilities, and it is unlikely there would be disagreement about the values.

Estimating probabilities using relative frequencies

Another method of estimating the probability of an event is to use the observed, or hypothetical, relative frequency of the event. The **relative frequency** of an event is the number of occurrences of the event divided by the number of times the event could have occurred. This is illustrated in Examples 1.2 to 1.4.

Example 1.2   Probability of Down's syndrome

In every pregnancy there is a risk that the foetus has Down's syndrome. The risk increases with maternal age, so an older mother is more likely to be carrying a foetus with Down's syndrome than is a younger mother.

Several large-scale surveys have been carried out to estimate, for different ages of the mother, the probability that a foetus has Down's syndrome. For each maternal age, data are available on the proportion of foetuses with Down's syndrome. These data provide a direct estimate of the relative frequency, and hence of the probability, of Down's syndrome for different ages of the mother. Table 1.1 (overleaf) shows estimates of $P(\text{Down's})$, the probability of Down's syndrome at 40 weeks' gestation, for different maternal ages.

These data were obtained in June 2004 from the website of the Fetal Medicine Foundation http://www.fetalmedicine.com.

9

Table 1.1   Estimated probability that a foetus
has Down's syndrome, by maternal age

Maternal age (years)	Estimate of $P(\text{Down's})$
20	1/1527
25	1/1352
30	1/895
31	1/776
32	1/659
33	1/547
34	1/446
35	1/356
36	1/280
37	1/218
38	1/167
39	1/128
40	1/97
41	1/73
42	1/55
43	1/41
44	1/30
45	1/23

Note that the probabilities in Table 1.1 are *estimates* and may not be equal to the
true, underlying values of the probabilities. However, they are estimated from
large amounts of data, so they should be very good estimates.   ◆

Example 1.3   Probability of a volcanic eruption

In January 1993, a conference on predicting volcanic eruptions was held at the
foot of the Galeras volcano in Colombia. The highlight of the conference was to
be a trip into the crater. After much debate concerning the risk (that is, the
probability) of Galeras erupting, the trip went ahead. However, Galeras erupted
during the trip, killing six scientists and three tourists.

Aspinall, W.P., Woo, G.,
Voight, B., Baxter, P.J. *et al.*
(2003) Evidence-based
volcanology: application to
eruption crises. *Journal of
Volcanology and Geothermal
Research*, **128**, 273–285.

Suppose that prior to the trip into the crater, an estimate was required of the
probability of an imminent eruption, where 'imminent' is taken to mean within
the next seven days. How might a suitable estimate be obtained? One simple
method of estimating the probability of eruption within the next week is to use
data on previous eruptions to calculate the relative frequency of weeks in a year
when Galeras erupted.

Before January 1993, there was approximately one eruption per year, on average.
That is, out of the 52 weeks in a year there was one week, on average, in which
Galeras erupted. Therefore, assuming that eruptions do not follow any temporal
pattern — for example, all occurring in summer — an estimate of the relative
frequency of weeks with an eruption in a year is $\frac{1}{52}$. Therefore the probability of
an eruption being imminent can be estimated as $\frac{1}{52}$.   ◆

Since the estimates of $P(\text{Down's})$ in Example 1.2 were based on a large amount of
data, we can be fairly confident about them. However, the estimate of the
probability $P(\text{imminent eruption})$ in Example 1.3 was based on far less data, and
consequently we may be less confident about it. Indeed, it is possible that there
could be disagreement about its value — especially from expert volcanologists
who may have different knowledge about Galeras and volcanic behaviour. For
example, eruptions might not be independent events, in which case the recent
history of eruptions might affect the probability of an eruption in the next week.

In Example 1.4, the problem of estimating the probability that a defendant is
guilty in a court case is considered. In this example, there are no data that can be
used directly to calculate relative frequencies. Instead, relative frequencies need to
be hypothesized.

Example 1.4   *Probability of guilt*

Denis John Adams was tried on a charge of sexual assault in January 1995. Suppose that before any evidence from either the prosecution or the defence had been heard, the court wished to have an estimate of the probability that Adams is guilty.

Before any prosecution or defence evidence is presented, it might be reasonable to assume that the culprit is a male aged between 18 and 60. There were approximately 150 000 males of this age who lived locally to where the crime took place. Of course, the culprit may not be local. This increases the hypothesized number of possible men who could be the culprit from around 150 000 to 200 000, say. Before observing any evidence, Adams is known only to be one of the possible culprits, so $P(\text{Adams guilty})$ can be estimated to be $\frac{1}{200\,000}$.

It is possible that not everyone will agree with the estimate of $\frac{1}{200\,000}$ for $P(\text{Adams guilty})$. For example, the prosecution may argue that the hypothesized number of possible men who could be the culprit is much less than 200 000, so that the estimate for $P(\text{Adams guilty})$ should in fact be larger. ◆

Dawid, A.P. (2007) Statistics and the law. In Tybjerg, K., Swenson-Wright, J. and Bell, A. (eds) *Evidence*. Cambridge University Press.

Activity 1.2   *Coronary heart disease*

Coronary heart disease (CHD) is currently the most common cause of death in the UK. In 2002, of 288 332 male deaths, 64 473 were from CHD, and of 318 463 female deaths, 53 003 were from CHD.

(a) Estimate the following probabilities.

    (i)   The probability that a randomly chosen UK man who dies in a future year will die of CHD.

    (ii) The probability that a randomly chosen UK woman who dies in a future year will die of CHD.

(b) How accurate are your estimates likely to be?

These data were obtained in June 2004 from the British Heart Foundation Statistics website http://www.heartstats.org.

Estimating probabilities subjectively

In some situations, it may not be possible to observe, or even hypothesize, the relative frequency of an event. For example, an event may occur only very rarely or be a 'one-off' event. This is illustrated in Examples 1.5 and 1.6.

Example 1.5   *Avian influenza*

In 2006, the spread of the H5N1 influenza virus in birds caused widespread concern about the likelihood of a world epidemic (or pandemic) of this deadly type of influenza in humans. This would occur if the avian H5N1 influenza virus were to mutate so as to transmit easily between humans. Based on the current understanding of the biology of the influenza virus, and the observation that human pandemics of this type of influenza have occurred in the past, scientists are agreed that the chance of such a mutation occurring at some point in the future is high. However, there are no reliable frequency data from which to estimate directly the probability that this will occur in the next year. ◆

11

Example 1.6 US space missions

In January 2004, the US president George W. Bush unveiled a plan to return Americans to the moon by 2020, with the aim that this would be used as a stepping stone for a manned mission to Mars. Consider the following probabilities:

P(Americans return to the moon by 2020),

P(manned mission to Mars by 2035).

These are both probabilities of one-off events with no data available from which to estimate relative frequencies. ◆

The probabilities in Examples 1.5 and 1.6 cannot be estimated objectively. Any estimates of the probabilities will be subjective to some degree, and as such will reflect the opinions and beliefs of whoever is making the estimates. For this reason, Bayesian statistics often refers to probabilities as representing beliefs, or opinions, about a proposition. Naturally, whenever estimates are made subjectively, there may be disagreement about the estimates.

Estimating the probability of an event accurately can be difficult, especially if the person estimating the probability is not confident, or familiar, with using probabilities. To illustrate this, try estimating some probabilities yourself.

Activity 1.3 Position of the letter r

This activity concerns the use of the letter r in English words. The probabilities p_1 and p_3 are defined as follows:

$p_1 = P$(an English word begins with the letter r),

$p_3 = P$(an English word has r as the third letter).

Which of these two probabilities would you estimate to be the larger? Explain your answer.

Summary of Section 1

In this section, the estimation of probabilities has been discussed. The simplest way to estimate the probability of an event is to use the observed, or hypothesized, relative frequency of the event. When this is not possible, more subjective methods for obtaining probability estimates must be used. You have seen that estimating probabilities is not always easy.

Exercise on Section 1

Exercise 1.1 Children's lunchboxes

(a) In a study to investigate what UK children have in their packed lunches at school, 720 mothers were questioned. Of these mothers, 374 said that they packed crisps into their child's lunchbox every day. Estimate the probability that a UK schoolchild has crisps in their lunchbox every day.

(b) In another study, the contents of the lunchboxes of 28 UK children in a class were observed for one week. It was found that 19 of the children had crisps every day that week. Use data from this study to estimate the probability that a UK schoolchild has crisps in their lunchbox every day.

(c) Which of the estimates that you calculated in parts (a) and (b) do you think is the more reliable? Explain your answer.

2 Bayes' theorem

In this section, a result which is at the heart of Bayesian statistics is introduced. This result is known as Bayes' theorem. One of the key elements of Bayes' theorem is conditional probability; this is discussed in Subsection 2.1. Bayes' theorem is introduced in Subsection 2.2. You will see how it can be used to update beliefs about a proposition when data are observed or information becomes available. In fact, Bayes' theorem can be used repeatedly to update beliefs as additional data or information become available. This is illustrated in Subsection 2.3.

2.1 Conditional probability

Conditional probabilities were discussed briefly in the *Introduction to statistical modelling*. Since they are very important in Bayesian statistics, they will be considered further in this subsection. The ideas of conditional probability and independence are reviewed in Example 2.1.

Example 2.1 Heart disease and gender

The data on deaths from coronary heart disease (CHD) by gender, which were introduced in Activity 1.2, are summarized in Table 2.1.

Table 2.1   UK deaths in 2002 from coronary heart disease (CHD) by gender

Died from CHD	Gender Male	Female	Total
Yes	64 473	53 003	117 476
No	223 859	265 460	489 319
Total	288 332	318 463	606 795

Let the variable X represent the gender of a person who died, and let the variable Y indicate whether or not a person died from CHD. An estimate of $P(Y = \text{yes})$, the probability that a randomly chosen individual died from CHD, is given by

$$\frac{\text{number who died from CHD}}{\text{total number who died}} = \frac{117\,476}{606\,795} \simeq 0.1936.$$

Now suppose that the additional information that the person who died was male is available — that is, X takes the value 'male'. With this extra knowledge, $P(Y = \text{yes})$ is no longer the appropriate probability that death was due to CHD. The probability required can be estimated from the data in Table 2.1 on males who died:

You estimated this probability in Activity 1.2.

$$\frac{\text{number of males who died from CHD}}{\text{number of males who died}} = \frac{64\,473}{288\,332} \simeq 0.2236.$$

The probability that a person died from CHD (that is, Y takes the value 'yes'), when it is known that the person is male (X takes the value 'male') is the conditional probability $P(Y = \text{yes}|X = \text{male})$.

Recall that two random variables X and Y are independent if, for all values of x and y,

$$P(Y = y|X = x) = P(Y = y).$$

In this case, the estimated conditional probability that $Y = \text{yes}$, given $X = \text{male}$, is different from the estimated probability that $Y = \text{yes}$; that is,

$$P(Y = \text{yes}|X = \text{male}) \neq P(Y = \text{yes}).$$

Therefore X and Y may be dependent variables.   ◆

Activity 2.1   Conditional probabilities of Down's syndrome

Estimates of $P(\text{Down's})$, the probability that a foetus has Down's syndrome for different ages of the mother, were given in Table 1.1. The probabilities, which are reproduced in Table 2.2, are in fact the conditional probabilities $P(\text{Down's}|\text{mother's age})$.

(a) Use Table 2.2 to write down the following conditional probabilities.

   (i) $P(\text{Down's}|\text{mother's age} = 25 \text{ years})$

   (ii) $P(\text{Down's}|\text{mother's age} = 40 \text{ years})$

(b) Is it possible to conclude from your answers to part (a) that more foetuses with Down's syndrome occur in pregnant women aged 40 than in pregnant women aged 25?

Table 2.2   Estimated probability that a foetus has Down's syndrome, by maternal age

Maternal age (years)	Estimate of $P(\text{Down's})$
20	1/1527
25	1/1352
30	1/895
31	1/776
32	1/659
33	1/547
34	1/446
35	1/356
36	1/280
37	1/218
38	1/167
39	1/128
40	1/97
41	1/73
42	1/55
43	1/41
44	1/30
45	1/23

In general, if the probability that an event A occurs depends on whether or not an event B has occurred, then we speak of the **conditional probability of A given B**. The conditional probability is defined in the following box.

Conditional probability

For two events A and B, the **conditional probability** of A given B is denoted $P(A|B)$, and is defined by the formula

$$P(A|B) = \frac{P(A \text{ and } B)}{P(B)}. \tag{2.1}$$

The probability $P(A \text{ and } B)$ is the **joint probability** of A and B.

In Example 2.1, conditional probabilities were estimated from a contingency table. More generally, conditional probabilities can be calculated using Formula (2.1). This is illustrated in Example 2.2.

Example 2.2   Calculating a conditional probability

Data on deaths from CHD by gender were given in Example 2.1 (see Table 2.1). The variable X represents the gender of a person who died, and the variable Y indicates whether or not a person died from CHD. In Example 2.1, the conditional probability $P(Y = \text{yes}|X = \text{male})$ was estimated directly to be 0.2236. This probability could have been calculated using Formula (2.1), as follows.

First, estimates of the probabilities $P(Y = \text{yes and } X = \text{male})$ and $P(X = \text{male})$ are required. Using the data in Table 2.1,

$$P(X = \text{male}) = \frac{\text{number of male deaths}}{\text{total number of deaths}} = \frac{288\,332}{606\,795} \simeq 0.4752,$$

$$P(Y = \text{yes and } X = \text{male}) = \frac{\text{number of men who died from CHD}}{\text{total number of deaths}}$$
$$= \frac{64\,473}{606\,795} \simeq 0.1063.$$

Then Formula (2.1) gives

$$P(Y = \text{yes}|X = \text{male}) = \frac{P(Y = \text{yes and } X = \text{male})}{P(X = \text{male})} \simeq \frac{0.1063}{0.4752} \simeq 0.2237.$$

The slight discrepancy between this result and that obtained directly in Example 2.1 is due to rounding error. ♦

Activity 2.2   Calculating another conditional probability

(a) Use the data in Table 2.1 to estimate the conditional probability
$P(X = \text{male}|Y = \text{yes})$.

(b) The joint probability $P(Y = \text{yes and } X = \text{male})$ was estimated to be 0.1063
in Example 2.2. In Example 2.1, the probability $P(Y = \text{yes})$ was estimated to
be 0.1936. Use Formula (2.1) to estimate the conditional probability
$P(X = \text{male}|Y = \text{yes})$. Check that this estimate of the conditional
probability is the same as that obtained in part (a).

Using Formula (2.1), for any events A and B,

$$P(A|B) = \frac{P(A \text{ and } B)}{P(B)},$$

$$P(B|A) = \frac{P(A \text{ and } B)}{P(A)}.$$

Hence $P(A|B) = P(B|A)$ only when $P(A) = P(B)$. In general, for events A
and B,

$$P(A|B) \neq P(B|A).$$

The ordering of the conditioning is important. An illustration of this is given by
Example 2.2 and Activity 2.2: in Example 2.2, you saw that
$P(Y = \text{yes}|X = \text{male}) \simeq 0.2237$, whereas in Activity 2.2, you found that
$P(X = \text{male}|Y = \text{yes}) \simeq 0.5491$.

In some areas of application, misinterpreting the ordering of the conditioning can
have serious consequences. One such area is in court cases. In a court case, a
juror will vote for a guilty verdict only if he or she believes 'beyond reasonable
doubt' that the defendant is guilty — that is, if, after hearing all the evidence, he
or she assesses the probability that the defendant is guilty to be close to 1. The
jurors therefore need to estimate the conditional probability
$P(\text{defendant guilty}|\text{evidence})$. However, as you will see in Example 2.3, it can be
all too easy for a juror to interpret $P(\text{evidence}|\text{defendant guilty})$ as being the
same as $P(\text{defendant guilty}|\text{evidence})$. This is known as the 'prosecutor's fallacy'
as it can lead to a juror believing that the probability that the defendant is guilty
is larger than it actually is.

Example 2.3   The prosecutor's fallacy

The case of Denis John Adams, who was tried on the charge of sexual assault in
January 1995, was introduced in Example 1.4. The prosecution case rested on
forensic evidence, which will be called M:

$M = $ DNA match between Adams and a sample, accepted as
being from the culprit, taken from the victim.

The prosecutor's forensic expert testified that for a randomly chosen person, the
probability that their DNA matched that of the sample was $1/200\,000\,000$. The
defence argued that this probability was in fact $1/2\,000\,000$. It is tempting to
assign the value $1/200\,000\,000$ (or $1/2\,000\,000$) to the conditional probability
$P(\text{Adams not guilty}|M)$. If this is done then, since this probability is very small
— $1/200\,000\,000$ according to the prosecution, $1/2\,000\,000$ according to the defence
— and given that there is a DNA match, it would be reasonable to conclude that
Adams must be guilty. In fact, the probabilities of a DNA match provided by the
prosecution and defence were estimates of the conditional probability
$P(M|\text{Adams not guilty})$, which is not the same as $P(\text{Adams not guilty}|M)$.
Basing a verdict on the probability $P(M|\text{Adams not guilty})$ is incorrect: it is an
instance of the prosecutor's fallacy.   ♦

2.2 Bayes' theorem

Formula (2.1) can be rearranged to give a formula for the joint probability of A and B in terms of $P(B)$ and $P(A|B)$:

$$P(A \text{ and } B) = P(A|B) \times P(B). \tag{2.2}$$

However, the order of A and B in Formula (2.1) is arbitrary, so

$$P(B \text{ and } A) = P(B|A) \times P(A).$$

Since $P(A \text{ and } B) = P(B \text{ and } A)$, it follows that

$$P(A|B) \times P(B) = P(B|A) \times P(A).$$

Provided that $P(B) \neq 0$, dividing by $P(B)$ leads to an alternative formula for calculating a conditional probability:

$$P(A|B) = \frac{P(B|A) \times P(A)}{P(B)}. \tag{2.3}$$

The use of this formula to calculate a conditional probability is illustrated in Example 2.4.

Example 2.4 Using the alternative formula

Formula (2.3) can be used to obtain an estimate of the probability that a person who is known to have died of CHD is male, as follows:

$$P(X = \text{male}|Y = \text{yes}) = \frac{P(Y = \text{yes}|X = \text{male}) \times P(X = \text{male})}{P(Y = \text{yes})}.$$

In Example 2.1, $P(Y = \text{yes}|X = \text{male})$ was estimated to be 0.2236, and $P(Y = \text{yes})$ was estimated to be 0.1936. In Example 2.2, $P(X = \text{male})$ was estimated to be 0.4752. Therefore

$$P(X = \text{male}|Y = \text{yes}) \simeq \frac{0.2236 \times 0.4752}{0.1936} \simeq 0.5488.$$

This is the same as the estimate that you obtained in part (a) of Activity 2.2. ◆

You may be wondering why Formula (2.3) might be preferred to Formula (2.1) for calculating a conditional probability. The reason is that it is often easier to calculate $P(A \text{ and } B)$ using $P(B|A) \times P(A)$ than it is to calculate it directly. This is illustrated in Example 2.5.

Example 2.5 Probability of guilt given prosecution's evidence

In Example 2.3, you saw that the prosecution case against Denis John Adams rested on forensic evidence M of a DNA match. The judge and jury require an estimate of the probability that Adams is guilty, given the evidence M. Using Formula (2.1) for a conditional probability, this is given by

$$P(\text{Adams guilty}|M) = \frac{P(\text{Adams guilty and } M)}{P(M)}.$$

However, thinking about the joint probability $P(\text{Adams guilty and } M)$ is not easy! On the other hand, using Formula (2.3) for a conditional probability gives

$$P(\text{Adams guilty}|M) = \frac{P(M|\text{Adams guilty}) \times P(\text{Adams guilty})}{P(M)}.$$

First consider $P(M|\text{Adams guilty})$. If Adams is guilty, then the probability of a DNA match might be assumed to be very close to 1. (It might not be exactly 1 due to the possibility of errors in the DNA test.) For simplicity, set

$$P(M|\text{Adams guilty}) = 1.$$

In Example 1.4, $P(\text{Adams guilty})$ was estimated to be $1/200\,000$. Therefore

$$P(\text{Adams guilty}|M) \simeq \frac{1 \times \frac{1}{200\,000}}{P(M)}.$$

The problem of how to calculate $P(M)$ remains. The solution is to use another general result involving conditional probabilities. This is discussed below. ♦

If $P(M|\text{Adams guilty}) = 1$, then $P(M \text{ and Adams guilty})$ is equal to $P(\text{Adams guilty})$. In reality, $P(M|\text{Adams guilty})$ is not exactly 1, so these probabilities will not be exactly the same.

Calculating $P(B)$ in the denominator of Formula (2.3) can be tricky. However, conditional probabilities can be used to simplify its calculation, as follows.

When B occurs, either A occurs, or A does not occur. Therefore

$$P(B) = P(B \text{ and } A) + P(B \text{ and not } A).$$

Using Formula (2.2), this becomes

$$P(B) = P(B|A) \times P(A) + P(B|\text{not } A) \times P(\text{not } A). \tag{2.4}$$

This is the result needed. Activity 2.3 will give you some practice at using this formula.

Activity 2.3   Calculating the probability of CHD

Data concerning deaths from coronary heart disease and gender were given in Table 2.1.

(a) Use the data to estimate the conditional probability $P(Y = \text{yes}|X = \text{female})$.

(b) In Example 2.1, $P(Y = \text{yes}|X = \text{male})$ was estimated to be 0.2236, and in Example 2.2, $P(X = \text{male})$ was estimated to be 0.4752. Use these estimates and Formula (2.4) to calculate $P(Y = \text{yes})$.

Example 2.6   Probability of guilt given prosecution's evidence, continued

Formula (2.4) can be used to complete the calculation of the probability that Adams is guilty given evidence of a DNA match, which was begun in Example 2.5.

In that example, you saw that

$$P(\text{Adams guilty}|M) = \frac{P(M|\text{Adams guilty}) \times P(\text{Adams guilty})}{P(M)}$$

$$\simeq \frac{1 \times \frac{1}{200\,000}}{P(M)}. \tag{2.5}$$

Using Formula (2.4) to calculate $P(M)$ gives

$$P(M) = P(M|\text{Adams guilty}) \times P(\text{Adams guilty})$$
$$+ P(M|\text{Adams not guilty}) \times P(\text{Adams not guilty}). \tag{2.6}$$

In Example 2.5, $P(M|\text{Adams guilty})$ was set equal to 1, and the estimate used for $P(\text{Adams guilty})$ was $1/200\,000$. Also,

$$P(\text{Adams not guilty}) = 1 - P(\text{Adams guilty}) \simeq 1 - \frac{1}{200\,000} = \frac{199\,999}{200\,000}.$$

Two estimates of $P(M|\text{Adams not guilty})$ were given in Example 2.3 — the prosecution's estimate $(1/200\,000\,000)$ and the defence's estimate $(1/2\,000\,000)$. Using the defence's estimate in (2.6) gives

$$P(M) \simeq 1 \times \frac{1}{200\,000} + \frac{1}{2\,000\,000} \times \frac{199\,999}{200\,000}$$

$$= \frac{2\,000\,000}{2\,000\,000 \times 200\,000} + \frac{199\,999}{2\,000\,000 \times 200\,000}$$

$$= \frac{2\,199\,999}{2\,000\,000 \times 200\,000}.$$

Substituting this in (2.5) gives

$$P(\text{Adams guilty}|M) \simeq \left(1 \times \frac{1}{200\,000}\right) \Big/ \frac{2\,199\,999}{2\,000\,000 \times 200\,000}$$

$$= \frac{2\,000\,000}{2\,199\,999}$$

$$\simeq 0.91.$$

Note that although the probability of guilt given the prosecution's evidence M is high, it is not as high as that given by the prosecutor's fallacy — that is, $1 - 1/2\,000\,000 = 0.999\,999\,5$.

So far, only the prosecution's evidence M has been considered. None of the defence's evidence has been taken into account. That will be done in Subsection 2.3. ◆

Activity 2.4   Probability of guilt according to the prosecution

Use the method of Example 2.6 to calculate the probability that Adams is guilty given the prosecution's evidence M, using the prosecution's estimate of $1/200\,000\,000$ for $P(M|\text{Adams not guilty})$. With the prosecution's estimate, does Adams seem to be guilty 'beyond all reasonable doubt'?

Formulas (2.3) and (2.4) together comprise Bayes' theorem. As its name implies, this theorem is central to Bayesian statistics. It is stated formally in the following box.

Bayes' theorem

For two events A and B, provided that $P(B) \neq 0$,

$$P(A|B) = \frac{P(B|A) \times P(A)}{P(B)},$$

where

$$P(B) = P(B|A) \times P(A) + P(B|\text{not } A) \times P(\text{not } A).$$

Bayes' theorem gives a method of revising probability estimates as additional information becomes available. The additional information is the information that is being conditioned on. The probability before additional information becomes available is referred to as the **prior probability**, and the revised probability using the additional information is called the **posterior probability**.

It may be helpful to think of Bayes' theorem using the diagram in Figure 2.1.

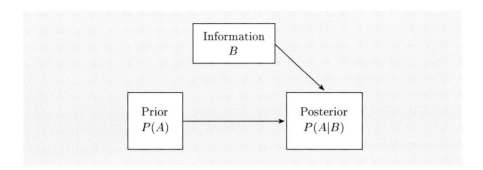

Figure 2.1   Bayes' theorem in practice

In the case of Adams' trial, the prior probability is $P(\text{Adams guilty})$, the initial estimate of the probability that Adams is guilty before any evidence is considered; the additional information (considered so far) is the prosecution's evidence M; and the posterior probability is $P(\text{Adams guilty}|M)$.

2.3   Sequential updating

Suppose that after observing information B, the posterior probability $P(A|B)$ has been calculated but now some additional information C is available. Bayes' theorem can be used to further revise the probability estimate. In this case, $P(A|B)$ becomes the *prior* probability, as this is the estimate *before* observing C. The posterior probability is $P(A|C, B)$. This can be calculated using Bayes' theorem:

$$P(A|C, B) = \frac{P(C|A, B) \times P(A|B)}{P(C|B)}, \tag{2.7}$$

where

$$P(C|B) = P(C|A, B) \times P(A|B) + P(C|\text{not } A, B) \times P(\text{not } A|B). \tag{2.8}$$

Notice that all the probabilities in (2.7) and (2.8) are conditional on B, since information B is now part of the prior information. It may be helpful to think of sequential updating in a Bayesian analysis using the diagram in Figure 2.2.

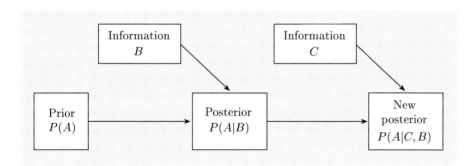

Figure 2.2   Sequential updating

Bayes' theorem can be used each time some additional information becomes available: whenever new data become available, the current posterior probability becomes the new prior probability.

The posterior probability that Adams is guilty, given the prosecution's evidence M, was calculated in Example 2.6. In Example 2.7, the defence's evidence is also considered, and the new posterior probability that Adams is guilty, given evidence from both the prosecution and the defence, is calculated.

Example 2.7   *Probability of guilt considering all the evidence*

In Example 2.6, the posterior probability that Adams is guilty, given the prosecution's evidence M, was calculated to be 0.91; that is, $P(\text{Adams guilty}|M) = 0.91$. This used the defence's prior estimate of $P(M|\text{Adams not guilty})$, which was $1/2\,000\,000$.

The defence case rested on two pieces of evidence, E_1 and E_2, where

$E_1 = $ victim said Adams did not look like her assailant,

$E_2 = $ Adams' girlfriend provided Adams with an alibi.

All items of evidence were considered to be independent of each other.

First, consider evidence E_1 — that the victim said her assailant did not look like Adams. The probability $P(\text{Adams guilty}|E_1 \text{ and } M)$ is required. The probability $P(\text{Adams guilty}|M)$ represents belief about Adams' guilt before considering evidence E_1, so this is the new prior. Bayes' theorem can be used to update the probability of guilt in the light of evidence E_1, as follows. Using (2.7) and (2.8) with all probabilities conditional on M,

$$P(\text{Adams guilty}|E_1 \text{ and } M)$$
$$= \frac{P(E_1|\text{Adams guilty}, M) \times P(\text{Adams guilty}|M)}{P(E_1|M)}, \tag{2.9}$$

where

$$P(E_1|M) = P(E_1|\text{Adams guilty}, M) \times P(\text{Adams guilty}|M)$$
$$+ P(E_1|\text{Adams not guilty}, M) \times P(\text{Adams not guilty}|M). \tag{2.10}$$

Items of evidence M and E_1 are considered to be independent of each other, so the DNA evidence M does not change the probability of E_1. Hence

$P(E_1|\text{Adams guilty}, M) = P(E_1|\text{Adams guilty}),$

$P(E_1|\text{Adams not guilty}, M) = P(E_1|\text{Adams not guilty}).$

If Adams really is guilty, the probability of E_1 would be low; it was thought to be about 0.1. On the other hand, if Adams is not guilty, the probability of E_1 would be high; it was thought to be around 0.9.

Substituting these values in (2.10) gives

Note that it is simply a coincidence that these probabilities sum to 1.

$$P(E_1|M) \simeq 0.1 \times 0.91 + 0.9 \times (1 - 0.91) = 0.172.$$

Then (2.9) becomes

$$P(\text{Adams guilty}|E_1 \text{ and } M) \simeq \frac{0.1 \times 0.91}{0.172} \simeq 0.53.$$

In the light of evidence E_1, the probability of Adams' guilt has dropped dramatically.

There is one final piece of evidence to consider — E_2, the fact that Adams' girlfriend provided him with an alibi. Taking this evidence into account, the probability required is

$P(\text{Adams guilty}|E_2, E_1 \text{ and } M).$

The probability $P(\text{Adams guilty}|E_1 \text{ and } M)$ becomes the new prior. The probability of guilt can be updated in the light of E_2 using Bayes' theorem:

$$P(\text{Adams guilty}|E_2, E_1, M)$$
$$= \frac{P(E_2|\text{Adams guilty}, E_1, M) \times P(\text{Adams guilty}|E_1, M)}{P(E_2|E_1, M)}, \tag{2.11}$$

where

$$P(E_2|E_1, M)$$
$$= P(E_2|\text{Adams guilty}, E_1, M) \times P(\text{Adams guilty}|E_1, M)$$
$$+ P(E_2|\text{Adams not guilty}, E_1, M) \times P(\text{Adams not guilty}|E_1, M). \tag{2.12}$$

Since all items of evidence were considered to be independent of each other,

$$P(E_2|\text{Adams guilty}, E_1, M) = P(E_2|\text{Adams guilty}),$$
$$P(E_2|\text{Adams not guilty}, E_1, M) = P(E_2|\text{Adams not guilty}).$$

The probability of E_2 if Adams is guilty was thought to be about 0.25, and the probability of E_2 if Adams is not guilty was thought to be about 0.5. Substituting these values in (2.12) gives

$$P(E_2|E_1, M) \simeq 0.25 \times 0.53 + 0.5 \times (1 - 0.53) = 0.3675,$$

and hence (2.11) becomes

$$P(\text{Adams guilty}|E_2, E_1, M) \simeq \frac{0.25 \times 0.53}{0.3675} \simeq 0.36.$$

Therefore, after all the evidence presented by both the prosecution and the defence has been considered, the probability that Adams is in fact guilty is only 0.36 — certainly not 'beyond reasonable doubt'!   ◆

Activity 2.5   Probability of guilt using prosecution's estimate

The final posterior probability $P(\text{Adams guilty}|E_2, E_1, M)$ depends on the value attached to $P(M|\text{Adams not guilty})$. The prosecution and defence did not agree on this value: the prosecution claimed that it is $1/200\,000\,000$, while the defence claimed it should be $1/2\,000\,000$. In Example 2.7, the value of 0.36 for the posterior probability that Adams is guilty was obtained using the defence's value of $1/2\,000\,000$.

See Example 2.3.

In Activity 2.4, you calculated $P(\text{Adams guilty}|M)$ to be 0.999 using the prosecution's value of $1/200\,000\,000$ for $P(M|\text{Adams not guilty})$. Use this result to calculate the posterior probability $P(\text{Adams guilty}|E_2, E_1, M)$. Is there now evidence of guilt 'beyond reasonable doubt'?

Summary of Section 2

In this section, conditional probabilities have been reviewed and Bayes' theorem has been introduced. When Bayes' theorem is used to calculate the conditional probability $P(A|B)$, the probability of event A given information B, the probability $P(A)$ is referred to as the prior probability, and the revised probability $P(A|B)$ as the posterior probability. You have seen that when new information C becomes available, Bayes' theorem can be used again, with $P(A|B)$ as the new prior probability, to find the new posterior probability $P(A|C, B)$.

Exercises on Section 2

Exercise 2.1   False positive HIV tests

HIV tests are not 100% accurate and they can produce a positive result for someone who is not infected with HIV. This is known as a false positive result. Although the probability of a false positive result is small, it can affect how the results of the test should be interpreted, especially for people who have a low risk of contracting HIV.

Tests can also produce a negative result for someone who is infected with HIV (known as a false negative result).

For simplicity, suppose that an HIV test gives a positive result for all people infected with HIV, so that it does not produce any false negative results. However, suppose that it does produce some false positive results, so that the test gives a positive result to 0.005% of people who are not infected with HIV.

(a) Calculate the following probabilities.

  (i)   The probability that a person who is infected with HIV will have a positive test result.

  (ii)   The probability that a person who is not infected with HIV will have a positive test result.

(b) Suppose that a woman in a low-risk group for contracting HIV takes the test. Only 10 in 100 000 women in this group are infected with HIV.

  (i)   Before taking the HIV test, what is the prior probability that the woman is infected with HIV?

  (ii)   Given that the woman has a positive test result, calculate the posterior probability that she is infected with HIV. Would you conclude that the woman is infected with HIV?

Exercise 2.2   *Searching for a wrecked ship*

In May 1968, the US nuclear submarine USS Scorpion (SSN-589) failed to arrive as expected at Norfolk, Virginia, USA, and was presumed wrecked. A team of mathematical consultants was used during the subsequent search. The sea was divided into grid squares, and a number was assigned to each square representing the probability that the wreck was in the square. The grid square with the highest probability of containing the wreck was then searched first. Although the wreck was not found in the first square searched, it was still possible that the wreck was in the square. The posterior probability that the wreck was in the square, given that it was not found, was calculated using Bayes' theorem (and the other grid square probabilities were updated accordingly, so that all the probabilities added up to 1). The second square to be searched was the one which now had the highest probability of containing the wreck. This process of searching squares and updating probabilities continued until the wreck was eventually found (in October 1968).

Information regarding USS Scorpion (SSN-589) was taken from the website of Wikipedia, The Free Encyclopedia, http://en.wikipedia.org in August 2006.

Suppose that the prior probability that the wreck is in a particular grid square is 0.4, and that the probability of finding the wreck in this grid square if it is there is 0.75. Given that the wreck is not found in this grid square, calculate the posterior probability that the wreck is in the grid square.

Exercise 2.3   *Haemophilia*

Haemophilia is an inherited disease which affects only males. Although females are not affected by haemophilia, they can be carriers of the disease. If a female carrier has a son, the probability that the son is affected by haemophilia is 0.5. This probability is the same for each son a female carrier may have. If a female is not a carrier, then any son she may have will not be affected by haemophilia.

Suppose that it is not known whether or not a particular woman, called Kate, is a carrier. Suppose further that there is a history of haemophilia in her family, and that the probability that Kate is a carrier is 0.5.

(a) Kate has a son, Jack, who is not affected by haemophilia. Calculate the following probabilities.

  (i) $P(\text{Jack is not affected}|\text{Kate is a carrier})$

  (ii) $P(\text{Jack is not affected}|\text{Kate is not a carrier})$

(b) Given that Jack is not affected by haemophilia, calculate the posterior probability that Kate is a carrier.

(c) You are now told that Kate has a younger son, Luke, who is also unaffected by haemophilia. Using your result from part (b), calculate the new posterior probability that Kate is a carrier.

3 A framework for Bayesian inference

In this section, the main ideas of the Bayesian inference process are presented.

In Sections 1 and 2, beliefs about a proposition A were represented probabilistically through the prior probability $P(A)$. After additional information B became available, Bayes' theorem was used to update beliefs about A, as expressed by the posterior probability $P(A|B)$. In most statistical problems, interest focuses not on a proposition but on an unknown parameter θ. In Bayesian statistics, beliefs about any unknown parameter are also represented probabilistically. Initially, this is through what is known as the **prior distribution**. Prior distributions are the subject of Subsection 3.1.

In Subsection 3.2, conditional distributions are discussed. These are required for describing the Bayesian process of inference.

Additional information which may update beliefs about θ are usually in the form of observed data $x_1, x_2, \ldots, x_n$. The information regarding θ contained in the data is represented by the **likelihood function**. The likelihood function is introduced in Subsection 3.3.

In Section 2, Bayes' theorem was used to update beliefs about a proposition after additional information became available. Bayes' theorem can also be used to update beliefs about a parameter θ after data are observed. The updated beliefs are represented by the **posterior distribution**. The posterior distribution, which summarizes all the information available about θ after observing data, is the primary focus of Bayesian inference. The posterior distribution and how it can be calculated using Bayes' theorem is discussed in Subsection 3.4.

3.1 Prior distributions

In Section 1, you saw how beliefs about a proposition A are represented by the probability $P(A)$, which can be estimated subjectively. Beliefs about an unknown parameter θ are also represented probabilistically in Bayesian statistics. A subjective estimate can be made of the probability that the value of θ is θ_1, say — that is, of the probability $P(\theta = \theta_1)$, for some value θ_1.

If you are certain that $\theta = \theta_1$, then $P(\theta = \theta_1) = 1$. However, the value of θ is rarely known with certainty. Instead, there will be other values of θ that are possible. Usually, the possible values of θ are all values in some continuous interval. For example, if θ is a proportion, then the true value of θ could potentially be any value in the interval $[0, 1]$. However, for simplicity, first suppose that θ can only be one of a set of discrete values $\theta_1, \theta_2, \ldots, \theta_n$. For each possible value θ_i, the probability $P(\theta = \theta_i)$ can be estimated subjectively, so that $P(\theta = \theta_i)$ represents beliefs about whether or not $\theta = \theta_i$. If $P(\theta = \theta_i)$ is estimated for all possible values of θ_i, then these probabilities will form a probability distribution for θ. This probability distribution gives a probabilistic representation of all the available knowledge about the parameter θ, and is known as the **prior distribution**, or simply the **prior**.

Note that, although θ has a probability distribution, θ does not vary: it is not a random variable. As in classical statistics, the true value of θ is fixed but unknown. The probability distribution for θ represents *beliefs* about the true value of θ.

Example 3.1 gives a simple illustration of how beliefs about a parameter θ can be used to estimate individual probabilities $P(\theta = \theta_i)$, and hence a prior for θ.

Example 3.1 Cancer at Slater School

Slater School is an elementary school in California. Staff were concerned that there was a high number of cancers among staff at the school. They thought this might be due to high-voltage power cables running past the school.

It was estimated that, nationally, the probability of an individual developing cancer was 0.03. Let the parameter θ be the probability of developing cancer at Slater School. It is assumed that this probability is the same for each of the 145 members of staff at the school, and that staff members develop cancer independently. Since θ is a probability, all values between 0 and 1 are possible values of θ. However, for the sake of illustration, suppose that only four values of θ are possible: 0.03, 0.04, 0.05 and 0.06. If the value of θ is 0.03, this would mean that the cancer rate is the same at Slater School as it is nationally; the other three values (0.04, 0.05 and 0.06) represent a higher incidence of cancer than the national average.

There have been other studies investigating whether proximity to high-voltage transmission lines can cause cancer, but the results are inconclusive. Suppose that equal weight can be attached to both sides of the argument. Then it is equally likely that proximity to high-voltage power cables does not cause cancer — in which case $\theta = 0.03$, the same as the national rate — and that proximity to high-voltage transmission lines does cause cancer — so that $\theta > 0.03$. This information can be represented probabilistically as follows:

$$P(\theta = 0.03) = \tfrac{1}{2}, \quad P(\theta = 0.04 \text{ or } 0.05 \text{ or } 0.06) = \tfrac{1}{2}.$$

Suppose that there is no information to suggest that any of the values 0.04, 0.05 and 0.06 is more likely than any other. This can be expressed as

$$P(\theta = 0.04) = P(\theta = 0.05) = P(\theta = 0.06) = \tfrac{1}{6}.$$

A prior distribution has been defined for θ. The probability mass function $p(\theta)$ of this prior is shown in Table 3.1. ◆

Lavine, M. (1999) What is Bayesian statistics and why everything else is wrong. *Journal of Undergraduate Mathematics and its Applications*, **20**, 165–174.

Table 3.1 The p.m.f. of a prior distribution for θ

θ	0.03	0.04	0.05	0.06
$p(\theta)$	$\tfrac{1}{2}$	$\tfrac{1}{6}$	$\tfrac{1}{6}$	$\tfrac{1}{6}$

Activity 3.1 Cancer at Slater School

In Example 3.1, concerning the incidence of cancer at Slater School, what is the most likely value of θ based on the prior beliefs about θ?

In most cases, a parameter θ will take values over an interval (such as $\theta > 0$ or $-\infty < \theta < \infty$). So instead of having a probability mass function $p(\theta)$ defined at a discrete set of values $\theta_1, \ldots, \theta_n$, the prior distribution will have a probability density function $f(\theta)$, defined for all possible values of θ. This is called the **prior density**. From now on, unless specified otherwise, it will be assumed that the prior for θ is a continuous probability distribution.

In Example 3.1, when considering a small number of possible values of θ, it was possible to estimate the probability that θ takes each individual possible value. However, this cannot be done when θ can take values defined on an interval. Instead, a prior density must be estimated whose shape represents beliefs about θ. The general idea of how this might be done is illustrated in Example 3.2.

Example 3.2   Are politicians truthful?

In an opinion poll, a number of adults in Great Britain were asked whether or not they trust politicians to tell the truth. Let θ be the unknown proportion of individuals who trust politicians to tell the truth; since θ is a proportion, it takes values between 0 and 1. Therefore, to represent prior beliefs about θ, a probability density function $f(\theta)$ must be defined for θ in the interval $[0, 1]$.

Guardian, 23 March 2004.

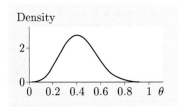

Suppose that you believe that θ is unlikely to be smaller than 0.05, or bigger than 0.9, and that you believe the most likely value of θ is 0.4. A sketch of a possible prior density representing these beliefs about θ is given in Figure 3.1. Notice that the density lies almost entirely between the values 0.05 and 0.9, because it is thought that θ is unlikely to be smaller than 0.05 or larger than 0.9. Also, the prior density peaks at the value $\theta = 0.4$, as 0.4 is believed to be the most likely value of θ.

Figure 3.1   A possible prior density for θ

Now suppose that you believe that the most likely value of θ is 0.4, but that θ is unlikely to be smaller than 0.3 or larger than 0.5. A sketch of a second possible prior density is shown in Figure 3.2. The prior densities in Figures 3.1 and 3.2 both have a peak at $\theta = 0.4$, as this is thought to be the most likely value of θ in both cases. However, since the area under the graph of $f(\theta)$ is 1 for both densities (because $f(\theta)$ is a probability density function), and the range of possible values of θ is smaller for the density in Figure 3.2, this prior density is narrower and taller than the prior density in Figure 3.1. The narrower prior density in Figure 3.2 represents a stronger belief that θ is close to 0.4 than that represented by the prior density in Figure 3.1.   ◆

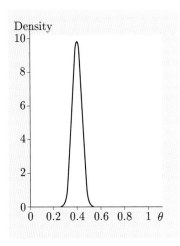

In general, the more uncertain you are about the value of θ, the flatter and wider your prior density should be. Conversely, the more confident you are about the value of θ, the taller and narrower your prior density should be. If you are uncertain about the value of θ, and hence have chosen a prior density that is quite flat, then this prior is said to be **weak**. On the other hand, if you are fairly confident about the value of θ (so that your prior density is tall and narrow), then this prior is said to be **strong**. Thus the prior in Figure 3.2 is stronger than the prior in Figure 3.1.

Figure 3.2   Another possible prior density for θ

Activity 3.2   Sketching prior densities

In Example 3.2, θ is the proportion of individuals in Great Britain who trust politicians to tell the truth.

(a) Sketch a possible prior density for θ if you believe that θ is unlikely to be smaller than 0.1, and that the most likely value of θ is 0.8.

(b) Sketch a possible prior density for θ if you believe that the most likely value of θ is 0.8, but that θ is unlikely to be smaller than 0.65 or larger than 0.9. Compare your prior density with the prior density you sketched in part (a).

(c) Sketch a possible prior density for θ if you are almost certain that θ is 0.8.

(d) Sketch the prior density for θ if you believe that all values between 0 and 1 are equally likely.

(e) Which of the four prior densities in parts (a) to (d) is the weakest? Order the four densities from weak to strong.

3.2   Conditional distributions

In Section 2, you saw that updating beliefs about a proposition involves the use of conditional probabilities. Updating beliefs about a parameter θ requires the use of conditional distributions. These are discussed briefly in this subsection. The idea of a conditional distribution is introduced in Example 3.3 for a situation where the random variables are discrete.

Example 3.3   Conditional distribution of CHD, given gender

Data on deaths from coronary heart disease (CHD) by gender were introduced in Example 2.1. The variable X represents the gender of a person who died, and Y indicates whether or not a person died from CHD. In Example 2.1, the conditional probability that $Y = $ yes, given that $X = $ male, was estimated to be 0.2236. Thus, as Y takes only two possible values, yes and no,

$$P(Y = \text{no}|X = \text{male}) = 1 - P(Y = \text{yes}|X = \text{male})$$
$$\simeq 1 - 0.2236 = 0.7764.$$

The two probabilities $P(Y = \text{yes}|X = \text{male})$ and $P(Y = \text{no}|X = \text{male})$ determine the **conditional distribution** of Y, given $X = $ male.   ◆

Activity 3.3   Conditional distribution of gender, given CHD

(a)   In Activity 2.2, you estimated the probability $P(X = \text{male}|Y = \text{yes})$ to be 0.5488. Hence obtain the conditional distribution of X, given $Y = $ yes.

(b)   In Example 2.2, the probability $P(X = \text{male})$ was estimated to be 0.4752. Hence verify that the distribution of X is not the same as the conditional distribution of X, given $Y = $ yes.

For discrete random variables X and Y, the conditional distribution of Y, given $X = x_0$, is a discrete distribution, so it has an associated probability mass function; this is denoted $p(y|X = x_0)$. Conditional distributions are defined analogously for continuous random variables X and Y. In this case, the conditional distribution of Y, given $X = x_0$, has a probability density function which is denoted $f(y|X = x_0)$.

Activity 3.4 involves the conditional distribution of a continuous random variable, given the value of a discrete random variable.

Activity 3.4   Nuchal translucency measurements, given Down's

When a foetus is aged between 11 and 14 weeks, a nuchal translucency scan can be carried out; this measures the fluid at the back of the baby's neck (the nuchal translucency). This measurement is associated with the length from the crown to the rump of the foetus. The crown–rump measurement allows doctors to estimate the nuchal translucency thickness. A single measurement of a variable X is obtained, where X is the nuchal translucency thickness observed from the scan minus the expected nuchal translucency thickness estimated from the baby's crown–rump measurement.

The distribution of X for foetuses with Down's syndrome is quite different from the distribution for foetuses without Down's syndrome. Hence there are two conditional distributions of interest: the conditional distribution of X, given that the foetus has Down's syndrome, and the conditional distribution of X, given that the foetus does not have Down's syndrome. Their p.d.f.s may be written $f(x|\text{Down's})$ and $f(x|\text{not Down's})$. Plots of these two conditional probability density functions are given in Figure 3.3.

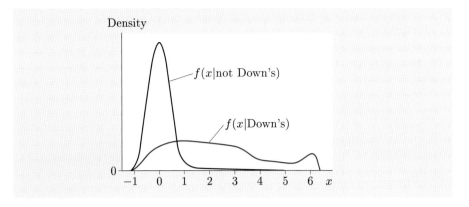

Source: Kypros H. Nicolaides (2004) 'The 11–13^{+6} weeks scan', Fetal Medicine Foundation, London.

Figure 3.3   Densities of X for foetuses with and without Down's syndrome

(a)   Is a value of X less than 0 more likely in a foetus with Down's syndrome or in a foetus without Down's syndrome? Explain your answer.

(b)   Is a value of X greater than 2 more likely in a foetus with Down's syndrome or in a foetus without Down's syndrome? Explain your answer.

3.3   The likelihood function

Suppose that the random variable X has some distribution with unknown parameter θ. If it were known that the value of θ is θ_0, then the distribution of X would be known exactly. If X is discrete then, *conditional on $\theta = \theta_0$*, the (conditional) probability mass function $p(x|\theta = \theta_0)$ can be written down. Similarly, if X is continuous, the conditional probability density function $f(x|\theta = \theta_0)$ can be written down.

In the Bayesian framework, θ has a distribution, so statements such as 'conditional on $\theta = \theta_0$' make sense.

This is illustrated in Example 3.4 for a situation where X is discrete.

Example 3.4   Are politicians truthful?

In Example 3.2, θ was defined to be the proportion of individuals in Great Britain who trust politicians to tell the truth. In the opinion poll mentioned in that example, 2004 adults were interviewed. However, to simplify the calculations, consider just the first 50 adults interviewed. The number of individuals who said that they trusted politicians to tell the truth is a single observation on a random variable X which can be modelled by the binomial distribution $B(50, \theta)$. Hence, if it is known that θ is some value θ_0, then the distribution of X is also known. Its p.m.f. is

$$p(x|\theta = \theta_0) = \binom{50}{x} \theta_0^x (1 - \theta_0)^{50-x}, \quad x = 0, 1, \ldots, 50.$$

For example, for $\theta_0 = 0.3$,

$$P(X = x|\theta = 0.3) = \binom{50}{x} 0.3^x 0.7^{50-x}. \quad \blacklozenge$$

Activity 3.5   Are politicians truthful?

Write down the probability mass function of X, given that $\theta = 0.2$, where X and θ are as defined in Example 3.4.

Of course, in Example 3.4 and Activity 3.5, it is not known that θ is 0.3 or 0.2, or indeed what its value is. In general, the value of a parameter θ of interest is not known. However, if X is discrete, the conditional p.m.f. $p(x|\theta = \theta_0)$ for different values of θ_0 can be used to help decide which values of θ are most likely for the observed data, and which are unlikely. Similarly, if X is continuous, the conditional p.d.f. $f(x|\theta = \theta_0)$ can be used.

First, consider the case where X is modelled by a discrete distribution with unknown parameter θ. Suppose that the single data value $X = x_1$ has been observed. For two possible values of θ, θ_1 and θ_2, the associated conditional probabilities are $P(X = x_1|\theta = \theta_1)$ and $P(X = x_1|\theta = \theta_2)$. Suppose that

$$P(X = x_1|\theta = \theta_1) > P(X = x_1|\theta = \theta_2).$$

This means that the probability of observing x_1 is larger if $\theta = \theta_1$ than if $\theta = \theta_2$. Therefore, the value $\theta = \theta_1$ explains the data better than the value $\theta = \theta_2$. In other words, as x_1 has been observed, θ_1 is a 'more likely' value for θ than θ_2.

Similarly, if X is modelled by a continuous distribution with unknown parameter θ then, given the observed value x_1 of X,

$$f(x_1|\theta = \theta_1) > f(x_1|\theta = \theta_2)$$

implies that θ_1 is a more likely value for θ than θ_2.

Example 3.5   Which value of θ is more likely?

In the poll described in Example 3.4, 22% of the 2004 adults interviewed said that they trusted politicians to tell the truth. Suppose that for the first 50 individuals interviewed, the observation $X = 11$ is obtained.

Consider two possible values of the parameter θ, $\theta = 0.2$ and $\theta = 0.3$. For the observed value $X = 11$,

$$P(X = 11|\theta = 0.2) = \binom{50}{11} 0.2^{11} 0.8^{39} \simeq 0.127,$$

$$P(X = 11|\theta = 0.3) = \binom{50}{11} 0.3^{11} 0.7^{39} \simeq 0.060.$$

Since

$$P(X = 11|\theta = 0.2) > P(X = 11|\theta = 0.3),$$

θ is more likely to be 0.2 than 0.3, for the observation $X = 11$.   ◆

Activity 3.6   Which value of θ is more likely?

Suppose that in Example 3.5, instead of $X = 11$, the observation $X = 14$ was made. In this case, $P(X = 14|\theta = 0.2) \simeq 0.050$ and $P(X = 14|\theta = 0.3) \simeq 0.119$. Which value of θ is more likely, given the observation $X = 14$, $\theta = 0.2$ or $\theta = 0.3$? Explain your answer.

Given an observation x on a discrete random variable X, the value of the conditional p.m.f. $p(x|\theta = \theta_0)$ can be calculated for each possible value θ_0 of θ. Since a value is defined for each possible value of θ, these values can be viewed as values of a function of θ, which can be written $p(x|\theta)$. This function is called the **likelihood function**, or simply the **likelihood**. It represents how likely the possible values of θ are for the observed data x.

When viewed as a function of x, the notation $p(x|\theta)$ represents the conditional p.m.f. of X given θ; when viewed as a function of θ, $p(x|\theta)$ is the likelihood function given the observation $X = x$. Therefore, to emphasize that the likelihood is a function of θ, and to distinguish it from the probability mass function $p(x|\theta)$, which is a function of x, the likelihood for θ is denoted $L(\theta)$.

Example 3.6   The likelihood function

In Example 3.5, the observed value of X was 11. For this observed value, the likelihood function is

$$L(\theta) = P(X = 11|\theta) = \binom{50}{11} \theta^{11}(1 - \theta)^{39}.$$

This function of θ is defined for all values of θ in the interval $[0, 1]$. A plot of the likelihood function is shown in Figure 3.4. Notice that although X is a discrete random variable with discrete probability mass function $p(x|\theta)$, the likelihood function is continuous, because it is a function of θ, and θ can take any value in the interval $[0, 1]$. The likelihood function has a peak when $\theta = 0.22$, the observed proportion of adults who said they trust politicians to tell the truth. This means that when 22% of the replies are observed to be 'yes', the most likely value of θ is 0.22. For values of θ greater than 0.5, the likelihood is close to 0. Therefore it is not likely that the true value of θ is greater than 0.5 when only a small proportion (22%) of 'yes' replies has been observed.   ◆

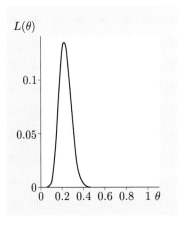

Figure 3.4   The likelihood function for θ given $X = 11$

Activity 3.7   Calculating a simple likelihood function

In Example 3.1, θ was the probability of developing cancer at Slater School. For simplicity, it was assumed that there are only four possible values of θ: 0.03, 0.04, 0.05 and 0.06.

There were 145 staff at Slater School. Let the variable X represent the number of staff who developed cancer at the school.

(a) What are the four possible probability models for X? Write down the p.m.f. of the model corresponding to $\theta = 0.03$.

(b) There were 8 cases of cancer among the staff at Slater School. The values of the likelihood function for the four possible values of θ given the observed value $X = 8$ are shown in Table 3.2.

Table 3.2   Values of the likelihood function

θ	0.03	0.04	0.05	0.06
$L(\theta)$	0.040	0.097	0.138	0.139

Of the four values of θ, which is the most likely given the observation $X = 8$? Which is the least likely value for θ?

In reality, the set of possible values of θ is almost always a continuous interval, so the likelihood function will be continuous.

The likelihood function $L(\theta)$ is defined analogously when X is a continuous random variable: the only difference is that the conditional p.m.f. $p(x|\theta = \theta_0)$ is replaced by the conditional p.d.f. $f(x|\theta = \theta_0)$ in its derivation. Given an observation $X = x$, the likelihood is the function of θ defined by $L(\theta) = f(x|\theta)$.

More generally, in a statistical inference problem, the data consist of n independent observations $x_1, \ldots, x_n$ on X. In this case, the likelihood is of the following form:

$$L(\theta) = p(\text{data}|\theta) = p(x_1|\theta) \times \cdots \times p(x_n|\theta) \quad \text{if } X \text{ is discrete,}$$
$$L(\theta) = f(\text{data}|\theta) = f(x_1|\theta) \times \cdots \times f(x_n|\theta) \quad \text{if } X \text{ is continuous.}$$

Whatever form the data take, the general form of the likelihood function $L(\theta)$ is the same, namely $p(\text{data}|\theta)$ or $f(\text{data}|\theta)$, viewed as a function of θ, over all possible values of θ. The details of calculating likelihood functions will be omitted: you will not be expected to calculate likelihood functions in this course. However, the likelihood function is a key element of a Bayesian analysis.

The main ideas concerning the likelihood function that are used in this book are summarized in the following box.

The likelihood function

The likelihood function for an unknown parameter θ is given by

$$L(\theta) = \begin{cases} p(\text{data}|\theta) & \text{for discrete data,} \\ f(\text{data}|\theta) & \text{for continuous data,} \end{cases} \tag{3.1}$$

where $p(\text{data}|\theta)$, or $f(\text{data}|\theta)$, is viewed as a function of θ, over all possible values for θ.

For two possible values of θ, θ_1 and θ_2, if

$$L(\theta_1) > L(\theta_2),$$

then for the observed data, θ_1 is a more likely value of θ than θ_2.

3.4 Posterior distributions

In Section 2, Bayes' theorem was used to update $P(A)$, the prior probability of an event A, given the information that event B has occurred. This was done by calculating the conditional probability $P(A|B)$, which is the posterior probability of A, given B.

Now suppose that we have an unknown parameter θ and its prior distribution representing our subjective beliefs about the possible values for θ. We want to use some data to make inferences about θ. So after observing data, we wish to update the prior distribution for θ, taking the data into consideration. This requires finding the conditional distribution of θ given the observed data. As the conditional distribution of θ given the data represents our updated subjective beliefs about θ after observing the data, it is called the **posterior distribution**, or simply the **posterior**, for θ. The associated p.d.f. is called the **posterior density**.

Possible values of θ almost always lie in a continuous interval, so both the prior and posterior distributions for θ are continuous with associated p.d.f.s $f(\theta)$ and $f(\theta|\text{data})$, respectively. The posterior density can be found using **Bayes' theorem for distributions**, which has the following general form:

$$f(\theta|\text{data}) = \begin{cases} \dfrac{p(\text{data}|\theta)f(\theta)}{p(\text{data})} & \text{for discrete data,} \\[2ex] \dfrac{f(\text{data}|\theta)f(\theta)}{f(\text{data})} & \text{for continuous data.} \end{cases} \tag{3.2}$$

The denominator is not a function of θ; it is constant whatever the true value of θ. Since interest lies primarily in the *shape* of the posterior density, the precise value of this constant is not of interest. Therefore (3.2) is often written as

$$f(\theta|\text{data}) \propto \begin{cases} p(\text{data}|\theta)f(\theta) & \text{for discrete data,} \\ f(\text{data}|\theta)f(\theta) & \text{for continuous data.} \end{cases} \tag{3.3}$$

The symbol '$\propto$' means 'is proportional to'.

Since, from (3.1), $f(\text{data}|\theta)$ (or $p(\text{data}|\theta)$) is the likelihood of θ, (3.3) may be written as

$$f(\theta|\text{data}) \propto L(\theta)f(\theta). \tag{3.4}$$

Bayesian inference is based on the properties of the posterior distribution.

Since (3.4) describes (up to some constant) the relationship between the posterior density $f(\theta|\text{data})$, the prior density $f(\theta)$ and the likelihood $L(\theta)$, it is often written in words as

posterior $\propto$ likelihood $\times$ prior.

The posterior distribution combines two sources of information about θ — the prior distribution, which represents prior subjective beliefs about θ, and the likelihood function, which represents the information about θ provided by the data. Therefore, in principle, the posterior distribution contains all the available information. It is used for estimating parameters, making predictions, or any other purpose for which the data were gathered. The relationship between the posterior, the prior and the likelihood, which lies at the heart of Bayesian inference, is summarized in the following box.

Bayesian inference

Bayesian inference is based on the posterior distribution for θ, given the data, denoted $f(\theta|\text{data})$. This is obtained from the prior density $f(\theta)$ and the likelihood $L(\theta)$ using the following expression:

$$f(\theta|\text{data}) \propto L(\theta)f(\theta),$$

or, in words,

posterior $\propto$ likelihood $\times$ prior.

In a Bayesian analysis, the prior distribution, which encapsulates prior beliefs, is combined with the likelihood, which summarizes the information contained in observed data, using Bayes' theorem, to give the posterior distribution. This is used to calculate estimates and make inferences. This process is represented in Figure 3.5.

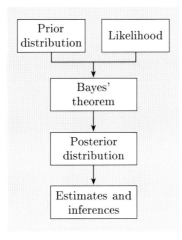

Figure 3.5   The process of a Bayesian analysis

Example 3.7   Bayesian analysis

A possible prior for θ, the proportion of individuals in Great Britain who trust politicians to tell the truth, was shown in Figure 3.1. The likelihood function for θ after observing 11 'yes' replies from 50 interviewees ($X = 11$) was given in Figure 3.4 (see Example 3.6).

See Example 3.2.

31

Figure 3.6 shows the prior, the likelihood and the resulting posterior for θ.

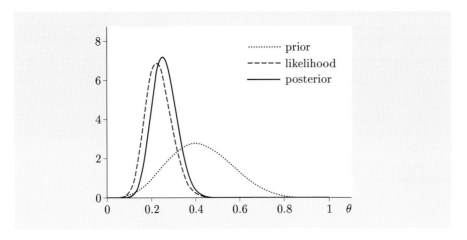

Figure 3.6   Prior, likelihood and posterior for θ

Since the prior and the posterior are distributions, the area under their densities is 1. In Figure 3.6, the likelihood has been scaled so that the area underneath it is also 1. This makes it easier to see how the prior and the likelihood combine to produce the posterior. Notice that the posterior lies between the prior and the likelihood: since the posterior combines information from the prior and from the data, as represented by the likelihood, it will always lie between the prior and the likelihood, as in Figure 3.6. Notice also that the posterior is much closer to the likelihood than to the prior, because the amount of information contained in the data is much greater than that contained in the prior. In this sense, the likelihood is stronger than the prior.

From now on, all plots of likelihoods will be scaled in this way.

The posterior density in Figure 3.6 summarizes all information about θ after observing $X = 11$. Prior to observing the data, it was believed that the most likely value of θ was 0.4 — the peak of the prior is at 0.4 — and that the value of θ was between 0.05 and 0.9. The posterior density is much narrower than the prior, so after observing the data, we are more confident about the value of θ. The posterior density represents the belief that θ lies between 0.1 and about 0.45. The most likely value of θ is now believed to be 0.25.   ◆

Since the posterior density $f(\theta|\text{data})$ represents what is known about θ after the data have been observed, it is used to make inferences about θ. In any Bayesian analysis, it is always a good idea to obtain a plot of $f(\theta|\text{data})$, as this gives an overall graphical summary of the posterior information about θ. Measures of location and spread of the posterior density can also be very useful.

The process of obtaining the posterior distribution and using it for inference is generally referred to as **prior to posterior analysis**. In Section 4, you will carry out a prior to posterior analysis for a proportion θ.

Summary of Section 3

In this section, a framework for Bayesian inference has been introduced. The prior distribution for a parameter θ, which has p.d.f. $f(\theta)$, summarizes beliefs about the value of a parameter θ before data are observed. The likelihood function for θ, which is denoted $L(\theta)$, summarizes the information about θ contained in the observed data. The posterior distribution, which has p.d.f. $f(\theta|\text{data})$, represents what is known about θ after the data have been observed. The posterior density combines the two information sources about θ, the prior and the likelihood, via the expression

posterior $\propto$ likelihood $\times$ prior.

Exercise on Section 3

Exercise 3.1   Explaining the posterior

The prior, likelihood and posterior for three different prior to posterior analyses for a proportion θ are shown in Figure 3.7.

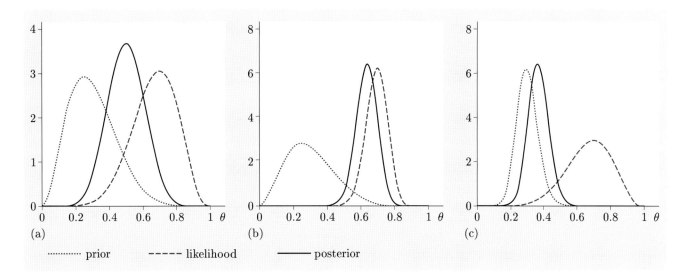

(a)   (b)   (c)

············ prior   ----- likelihood   ——— posterior

Figure 3.7   The prior, likelihood and posterior for a proportion θ: three analyses

For each prior to posterior analysis, explain why the posterior looks like it does in relation to the prior and the likelihood.

4   Exploring prior to posterior analyses for a proportion

In this section, you will use *LearnBayes* to explore the likelihood function for a proportion θ. You will calculate posteriors for given priors and likelihoods, and you will investigate how the prior and the likelihood affect the posterior.

Refer to Chapters 1 and 2 of Computer Book 4 for the work in this section.

Summary of Section 4

In this section, the software package *LearnBayes* has been introduced, and you have used *LearnBayes* to investigate prior to posterior analyses for a proportion. You have seen that the peak of the likelihood function always occurs when θ is equal to the observed proportion, and that as the sample size increases, the likelihood becomes narrower and hence more informative. You have also explored how the relative strengths of the prior and the likelihood determine the weight given to each by the posterior; you have seen that if enough data are available, the posterior looks like the likelihood however strong the prior is.

Part II   Prior to posterior analyses

Introduction to Part II

In Part I, the basic concepts involved in Bayesian statistics were introduced. The prior distribution describes the subjective beliefs formed before the data are gathered, and the likelihood contains the information provided by the data. You saw that these are combined using Bayes' theorem to form the posterior distribution using the expression

posterior $\propto$ likelihood $\times$ prior.

In Part II, prior to posterior analyses using some standard prior distributions are discussed. The mathematics involved in these prior to posterior analyses is fairly straightforward, and for this reason such analyses are widely used. You will perform your own prior to posterior analyses to learn about two parameters that are personal to you. You will specify your own priors for these parameters, collect some data, calculate the posteriors and use these to make inferences about the parameters. You will be asked to start collecting the data towards the end of Section 6. You should not postpone this activity as the data will take a week to collect and you will need the data in Subsection 9.3 (for the final computer session associated with Part II).

See Activity 6.7.

In Section 5, some standard families of prior distributions are described, together with the types of situation for which each is suitable. How these standard priors can be specified more precisely to represent opinions about an unknown parameter is the subject of Section 6. In Section 7, you will use *LearnBayes* to explore the standard priors and to specify your own prior distributions. The posterior distributions associated with each of the standard priors introduced in Section 5 are described in Section 8. The use of the posterior distributions to make inferences about unknown parameters is discussed in Section 9.

5 Using standard distributions as priors

Suppose that inferences are required about an unknown parameter θ, and that you wish to specify its prior density $f(\theta)$. You may have some idea of the general shape $f(\theta)$ should take to represent your prior opinions about θ; for example, you may have some idea of which value(s) of θ you believe to be the most likely, and therefore where the peak (or peaks) of $f(\theta)$ should be. You may also have some idea of the range of possible values of θ, and therefore for which values of θ you believe $f(\theta) > 0$. However, finding the mathematical form of a density which fits exactly the shape you may have in mind for the prior density may not be simple.

To avoid this problem, it is often convenient to use a standard distribution for $f(\theta)$. Of course, the standard distribution chosen may not represent your prior beliefs exactly. However, the approximation provided by a standard distribution is often good enough, especially considering that the prior represents subjective opinions which are seldom formulated very precisely.

In this section, four standard families of prior distributions are introduced: the normal family is discussed in Subsection 5.1, the uniform family in Subsection 5.2, the beta family in Subsection 5.3, and the gamma family in Subsection 5.4.

5.1 The normal prior

One distribution which is commonly used to represent prior opinions about an unknown parameter θ is the normal distribution. In this book, a normal prior will be denoted $N(a, b)$, where a is the mean and b is the variance of the distribution. Notice that the parameters for the normal distribution have been labelled a and b, rather than the more usual μ and σ^2. The reason for this is that priors may need to be defined for the normal parameters μ and σ^2 themselves, so to avoid confusion, when talking of a normal *prior*, the parameters a and b will be used.

The normal distribution is discussed in the Introduction to statistical modelling.

A sketch of the normal prior for a parameter θ is shown in Figure 5.1.

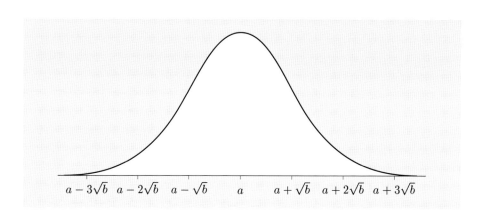

Figure 5.1 The normal prior $N(a, b)$

In this case,

$$\theta \sim N(a, b),$$

Note that b still represents a variance, even though there is no explicit 'square'.

where a and b are the prior mean and variance, respectively, of θ. Hence

$$f(\theta) = \frac{1}{\sqrt{2\pi b}} \exp\left(-\frac{1}{2b}(\theta - a)^2\right), \quad -\infty < \theta < \infty.$$

You do not need to remember this formula.

A key feature of the normal distribution is that it is symmetric about the mean a. Since the mode is also a, the most likely value of θ is a. Since $f(\theta) > 0$ for all values of θ, all values are theoretically possible. However, only values of θ for which $f(\theta)$ lies appreciably above zero are likely to occur. In practice, values more than three standard deviations from the mean — that is, less than $a - 3\sqrt{b}$ or greater than $a + 3\sqrt{b}$ — are very unlikely to occur. Thus the range of likely values for θ is $a \pm 3\sqrt{b}$.

Two situations in which a normal prior might be appropriate are described in Examples 5.1 and 5.2.

Example 5.1   Distance between London and Tokyo

What is the shortest distance from London to Tokyo, measured on the Earth's surface? Suppose that you have to guess the distance θ, without access to precise geographical records. You may be able to hazard a guess, but you are unlikely to know the distance precisely (to the nearest kilometre, say). Thus your prior distribution will peak at your best guess, but will be spread out on either side. Since you might be as likely to underestimate the distance as to overestimate it, a symmetric prior for θ might not be unreasonable. Thus a normal distribution might adequately represent your prior beliefs about the distance.   ♦

In Example 5.1, it would be fairly easy to obtain an accurate estimate of the distance between London and Tokyo, rather than to rely on guesswork. In Example 5.2, a situation in which such external information is not easily accessible is described.

Example 5.2   Memory tests

Surgical excision is a potential treatment for some patients suffering from temporal lobe epilepsy. A clinical neuropsychologist believes that surgery may have the undesirable side effect of impairing memory. To investigate this, a patient's memory must be tested both before having surgery and after surgery. However, the practice gained from the first test is likely to improve performance on the second test, so the effect of practice should be taken into account.

The neuropsychologist intends to give a test to a sample of patients and later repeat the test in order to estimate the benefit of practice. The test that will be used is the Delayed Memory Index of the Wechsler Memory Scale (a standard psychological memory test). So that the data are as relevant as possible, the sample will consist only of temporal lobe epilepsy patients who are suitable candidates for surgery, but who have not had surgery. This means that the sample size will be small.

The neuropsychologist is experienced, and has a good idea of the likely effect of practice. It is therefore decided to use this prior information in a Bayesian analysis, to supplement the (limited) information obtained from the small sample of data. Before the data are collected, the neuropsychologist is asked to specify her prior for θ, the mean improvement on the memory test of patients who do not have surgery.

The neuropsychologist believes that her prior for θ should be symmetric, so a normal prior may well be suitable.   ♦

Activity 5.1   Normal priors for the distance from London to Tokyo

In Example 5.1, a normal distribution was suggested as a possible prior for θ, the shortest surface distance between London and Tokyo (in thousands of kilometres). Two normal priors for θ are shown in Figure 5.2.

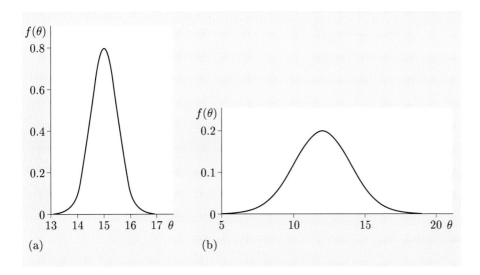

Figure 5.2   Two priors for the shortest distance between London and Tokyo

(a) For each of these two priors, identify the most likely value for θ.

(b) For each of the two priors, identify (i) the range of values that are possible for θ, and (ii) roughly, the range of values that are likely for θ.

(c) For which of the two priors in Figure 5.2 is b greater? How does the value of b reflect uncertainty about θ?

The normal prior is summarized in the following box.

The normal prior $N(a, b)$

The **normal prior** $N(a, b)$, with mean a and variance b, may be used to represent beliefs about θ that are symmetric about a single most likely value.

◇   Mode = median = mean = a.

◇   Variance = b.

◇   All values of θ in the range $-\infty < \theta < \infty$ are possible, but only those in the range $a \pm 3\sqrt{b}$ are likely.

5.2   The uniform prior

Another distribution which is commonly used for a prior is the (continuous) uniform distribution. Let a and b be two real numbers with $a < b$. If you are certain that θ lies within the interval $[a, b]$, but have no idea what the value of θ is within this interval, then your prior beliefs about θ can be represented by the uniform prior density on $[a, b]$.

The continuous uniform distribution is described in the *Introduction to statistical modelling*.

Example 5.3   *Distance between London and Tokyo, continued*

Suppose that you know that the circumference of the Earth is about 40 000 km, and that Tokyo lies somewhere between a quarter and half of the way round the Earth from London. Then it might be reasonable to represent your prior beliefs about θ, the distance from London to Tokyo, measured in thousands of kilometres, by the uniform prior density on the interval $[10, 20]$.   ◆

The uniform prior density is denoted $U(a, b)$, and its probability density function is given by

$$f(\theta) = \frac{1}{b - a}, \quad a \leq \theta \leq b. \tag{5.1}$$

A sketch of the uniform prior is given in Figure 5.3. Since the prior density is constant on $[a, b]$, it is sometimes called a *flat* prior.

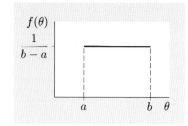

Figure 5.3   The uniform prior $U(a, b)$

Activity 5.2   *Sketching uniform priors*

Sketch the following priors, using Figure 5.3 as a guide.

(a) $U(-10, 10)$

(b) $U(1.5, 6.2)$

The uniform prior represents the opinion that every value of θ in the interval $[a, b]$ is equally likely, because $f(\theta)$ is constant between a and b. Also, all values of θ less than a and greater than b are impossible, because $f(\theta) = 0$ for such values.

When the interval $[a, b]$ is very wide, the uniform prior represents weak prior information about the parameter θ, because each possible value of θ between a and b is assigned the same probability, and therefore there is no value of θ in the interval $[a, b]$ that is believed to be more likely than any other. For this reason, the uniform prior can be used in a large number of situations to represent weak information about θ. However, note that if a and b are close together, then the uniform prior $U(a, b)$ represents strong information about θ. Thus the prior $U(10, 20)$ for the distance between London and Tokyo (in thousands of kilometres) represents rather weak prior information. However, the uniform prior $U(15, 15.5)$ for the same parameter represents rather strong beliefs about θ.

See Example 5.3.

Activity 5.3   *A uniform prior for memory test improvement*

In Example 5.2, θ was defined to be the mean improvement on the memory test of epilepsy patients who do not have surgery. Suppose that the neuropsychologist believes that the value of θ is greater than -20 and less than 30, but does not have any idea which value between these limits θ might take. Suggest a uniform prior to represent these opinions, and write down its probability density function.

Sometimes the maximum range of values that θ can take is obvious. For example, if θ is the probability that some specified event will occur, then θ must lie between 0 and 1. When θ is given a uniform prior on $[a, b]$, and $[a, b]$ is the complete range of values that θ could take, then the prior distribution is said to be **noninformative** as it does not provide any real information about the value of θ. For example, if θ is a probability, then the uniform prior on $[0, 1]$ is a noninformative prior for θ.

Example 5.4   *A noninformative prior for the distance from London to Tokyo*

The circumference of the Earth at the equator is $40\,076$ km. Thus no two points on the Earth can lie more than $20\,038$ km apart (with distances measured along the surface of the globe). In particular, London and Tokyo cannot lie more than $20\,038$ km apart. Thus the prior density $U(0, 20.038)$ for θ, the shortest surface distance between London and Tokyo (in thousands of kilometres), is noninformative.   ◆

In some circumstances, there is no obvious maximum range of values that θ can take. Nevertheless, it is possible to conceive of a prior distribution in which a takes an arbitrarily large negative value, and b an arbitrarily large positive value, without actually specifying the values of a and b. The corresponding uniform prior $U(a, b)$, with a arbitrarily large and negative and b arbitrarily large and positive, is called the **improper** uniform prior on $(-\infty, \infty)$. An improper uniform prior for a parameter θ can often be used when the range of θ is not known. Similarly, if a is known but b is not, the prior can be taken as uniform on $[a, b]$ with b an unspecified arbitrarily large value. This is the improper uniform prior on $[a, \infty)$.

A summary of the uniform prior is given in the following box.

> **The uniform prior $U(a, b)$**
>
> The **uniform prior** $U(a, b)$, with parameters a and b, may be used to represent the belief that the value of θ lies between a and b when it is not known which values within the interval $[a, b]$ are more likely than others.
>
> The uniform prior $U(a, b)$ is **noninformative** if the interval $[a, b]$ necessarily includes all values in the range of θ.
>
> **Improper** uniform priors may be used to represent lack of prior information about θ and its range.

5.3 The beta prior

Suppose that a prior is required for a proportion θ. As θ is a proportion, it must lie between 0 and 1. Example 5.5 shows that the normal and uniform priors may be inappropriate for a proportion.

Example 5.5   Are politicians trusted to tell the truth?

In Example 3.2, the parameter θ represented the proportion of individuals in Great Britain who trust politicians to tell the truth. Suppose that you believe that the most likely value of θ is 0.2, but that θ could be as large as 0.6. Your prior for θ needs to peak at $\theta = 0.2$, as this is the most likely value. This rules out a uniform prior, which does not have a 'most likely' value. What about a normal prior? The mode should be at $\theta = 0.2$. However, the prior needs to allow likely values up to at least $\theta = 0.6$. Since the normal prior is symmetric, it would allow likely values down to at least $\theta = -0.2$, as illustrated in Figure 5.4. Thus the normal prior would allow likely negative values. However, since θ is a proportion, all values of θ less than 0 are impossible. Consequently, the normal prior is inappropriate for representing these prior beliefs about θ.   ◆

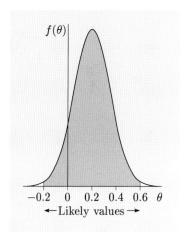

Figure 5.4   An inappropriate normal prior to represent beliefs about a proportion

A standard distribution which is often used as the prior for a proportion is the **beta distribution**. The beta distribution is often a suitable prior for a proportion θ, for two reasons. First, $f(\theta) > 0$ only for values of θ between 0 and 1. Secondly, the beta distribution can take a variety of shapes so that most prior distributions (with a single mode) on $[0, 1]$ are likely to be reasonably well approximated by a beta distribution.

The beta distribution, denoted $\text{Beta}(a, b)$, has two parameters, a and b, both of which are positive. The density for $\text{Beta}(a, b)$ is as follows:

$$f(\theta) = c \times \theta^{a-1}(1 - \theta)^{b-1}, \quad 0 \leq \theta \leq 1, \tag{5.2}$$

where c is a constant chosen so that the area under $f(\theta)$ is 1. The shape of the beta prior is determined by the values of a and b.

You do not need to remember this formula or know the value of c.

39

Activity 5.4 The Beta(1,1) prior

Use Formula (5.2) for the density of a beta distribution to obtain the density of the Beta$(1, 1)$ prior.

This density is the same as that of a member of one of the standard families that has already been described. Name the family and identify the values of the prior's parameters.

In Activity 5.4, you saw that the Beta$(1, 1)$ prior is the same as the $U(0, 1)$ prior, so it is a noninformative prior. But what does the Beta(a, b) prior look like for other values of the parameters a and b? Figure 5.5 shows the beta prior for various values of a and b.

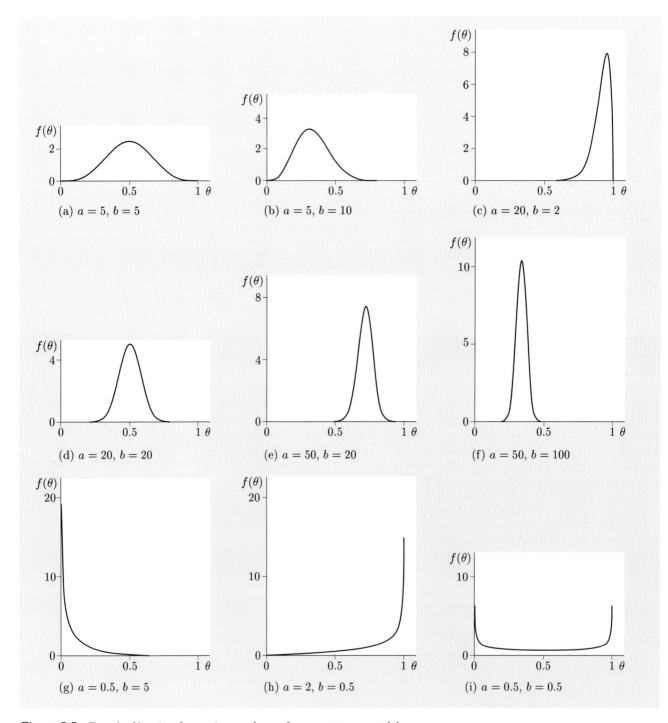

Figure 5.5 Beta(a, b) prior for various values of parameters a and b

Look across the top two rows of priors in Figure 5.5. Notice that, as a and b increase, the density gets narrower, representing stronger information about θ. As a and b decrease towards 1, the density gets flatter and wider, representing weaker information about θ.

Look again at Figure 5.5. Notice that the beta prior has a single mode when a and b are both greater than 1. In general, when $a > 1$ and $b > 1$, the mode is given by

$$\text{mode} = \frac{a-1}{a+b-2}. \tag{5.3}$$

When $a < 1$, there is a mode at 0, and when $b < 1$, there is a mode at 1. When $a < 1$ and $b < 1$, there are two modes — at 0 and 1. These cases are illustrated in the bottom row of priors in Figure 5.5.

Activity 5.5   Modes of beta priors

(a) Use Formula (5.3) to show that when $a = b$, the mode of the beta prior occurs at the point $\theta = 0.5$.

(b) Find the mode of each of the following priors.

   (i)   Beta$(5, 10)$

   (ii) Beta$(10, 5)$

   Show that the mode of Beta$(5, 10)$ is equal to one minus the mode of Beta$(10, 5)$.

Part (b) of Activity 5.5 provides an illustration of the following general result:

   mode of Beta$(a, b) = 1 -$ mode of Beta(b, a).

This result follows directly from Formula (5.3) for the mode of a beta distribution, since

$$\frac{a-1}{a+b-2} = 1 - \frac{b-1}{a+b-2}.$$

In fact, the probability density function of the Beta(b, a) distribution is a reflection of the p.d.f. of the Beta(a, b) distribution in the line $\theta = 0.5$. This is illustrated in Figure 5.6 for the priors Beta$(5, 10)$ and Beta$(10, 5)$.

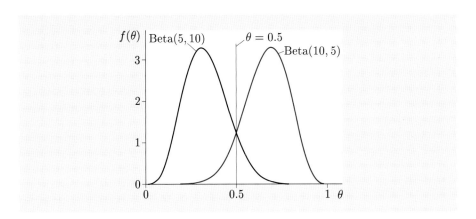

Figure 5.6   The Beta$(5, 10)$ and Beta$(10, 5)$ priors

As you saw in Figure 5.5, as a and b increase, the prior density gets narrower, representing stronger beliefs about the likely value of θ. The variance of Beta(a, b) is given by

$$\text{variance} = \frac{ab}{(a+b)^2(a+b+1)}.$$

For fixed mean, it can be shown that the larger the value of $a + b$ is, the smaller is the variance. Thus the value of $a + b$ determines how 'peaked' the prior is. Therefore if you have strong prior beliefs about θ, the value of $a + b$ should be large.

Example 5.6   Are politicians trusted to tell the truth?

In Activity 3.2, you sketched four prior distributions for θ, the proportion of persons who think that politicians can be trusted to tell the truth. Four priors were suggested in the solution to the activity. Their plots are reproduced in Figure 5.7.

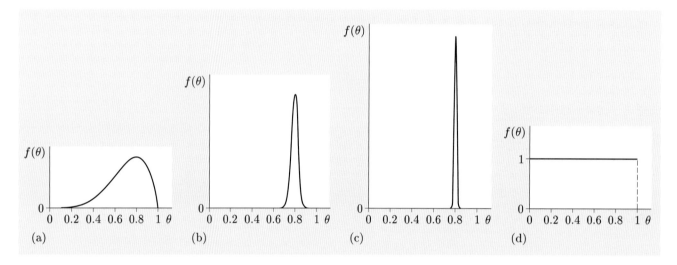

Figure 5.7   Four priors for θ

In fact, these priors are beta priors. Figure 5.7(a) shows the Beta$(5, 2)$ density, Figure 5.7(b) is the Beta$(110, 28)$ density, and the densities in Figures 5.7(c) and 5.7(d) are Beta$(1100, 280)$ and Beta$(1, 1)$, respectively. Thus the prior in Figure 5.7(c), with the largest value of $a + b$, represents the strongest beliefs about θ, whereas prior (d) represents the weakest beliefs.   ◆

Activity 5.6   Strength of beta priors

Verify that the beta priors Beta$(2, 4)$, Beta$(16, 46)$ and Beta$(26, 76)$ all have the same mode. Which prior represents the weakest prior beliefs, and which represents the strongest prior beliefs?

The beta prior is summarized in the following box.

The beta prior Beta(a, b)

The **beta prior**, with parameters $a > 0$ and $b > 0$, which is denoted
Beta(a, b), may be used to represent beliefs about a proportion θ, $0 \leq \theta \leq 1$.

◇   When $a > 1$ and $b > 1$, the beta density has a single mode, given by

$$\text{mode} = \frac{a - 1}{a + b - 2}.$$

◇   When $a < 1$, the beta density has a mode at 0. When $b < 1$, it has a
mode at 1. When $a < 1$ and $b < 1$, the density has two modes — at 0
and 1.

◇   The Beta($1, 1$) distribution is the same as the uniform distribution
$U(0, 1)$.

◇   The mean and variance of Beta(a, b) are given by

$$\text{mean} = \frac{a}{a + b}, \quad \text{variance} = \frac{ab}{(a + b)^2 (a + b + 1)}.$$

◇   The larger the value of $a + b$ is, the stronger are the beliefs represented
by the beta prior.

5.4   The gamma prior

Suppose now that the unknown parameter θ can take only positive values. How
should prior beliefs about θ be represented? A situation where the parameter of
interest can take only positive values is described in Example 5.7.

Example 5.7   Glass evidence in forensic science

Some crimes involve the criminal coming into contact with broken glass. For
example, burglaries frequently involve breaking a window, and hit and run cases
can involve headlamp and windscreen glass. In such crimes, glass particles often
transfer onto the criminal's clothing. However, members of the general public may
also have glass fragments on their clothes from non-criminal activities. Glass
particles from a suspect's clothing are routinely analysed by forensic scientists to
answer the question 'do the glass particles found on the suspect's clothes come
from the crime scene, or could they be consistent with what might be found
naturally on clothes in a given population?' Thus forensic scientists are interested
in the values taken by the parameter θ, where θ is the mean density of glass
fragments found naturally on clothes of members of the public.

The parameter θ is a density (of glass fragments), and hence can take only
non-negative values.   ◆

In Example 5.7, the parameter θ can take any value in the range $\theta > 0$, or
possibly $\theta \geq 0$. Thus a beta prior is inappropriate, since it applies to parameters
with the restricted range $[0, 1]$. Similarly, the uniform prior $U(a, b)$ is
inappropriate (unless the improper prior $U(0, \infty)$ is used). Example 5.8 shows
that a normal prior may also be inappropriate.

Example 5.8   Using a normal prior for a positive parameter

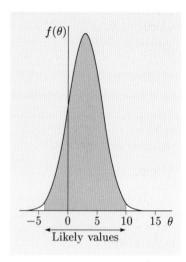

$f(\theta)$

Suppose that you believe that the most likely value for θ in Example 5.7 is 3 (measured in some unspecified units), but that θ could be as large as 10. Your prior for θ therefore needs to peak at $\theta = 3$ (as this is the most likely value) and allow for likely values up to at least 10. If a normal prior is to be used, with mode at 3, then since a normal distribution is symmetric about its mode, the prior must allow for likely values down to at least -4. This is illustrated in Figure 5.8.

However, θ cannot be negative, so $f(\theta)$ should be 0 for all $\theta < 0$. Therefore the normal prior is inappropriate for representing your beliefs about θ.   ♦

A standard distribution which is often used as a prior for a non-negative parameter is the **gamma distribution**. For the gamma distribution, $f(\theta) > 0$ for $\theta > 0$, so it is often suitable as a prior for a positive parameter θ. The gamma distribution has two parameters, a and b, both of which must be greater than 0. The gamma distribution with parameters a and b, which is denoted $\text{Gamma}(a, b)$, has the following probability density function:

$$f(\theta) = c \times \theta^{a-1} \exp(-b\theta), \quad \theta > 0, \tag{5.4}$$

where c is a constant which ensures that the area under $f(\theta)$ is 1. When $a = 1$, the gamma distribution is the same as the exponential distribution with parameter $\lambda = b$, and in this case $c = b$. Thus the exponential distribution is a special case of the gamma distribution.

Figure 5.9 shows the gamma prior for various values of a and b.

Figure 5.8   An inappropriate normal prior for θ

You do not need to remember this formula or know the value of c.

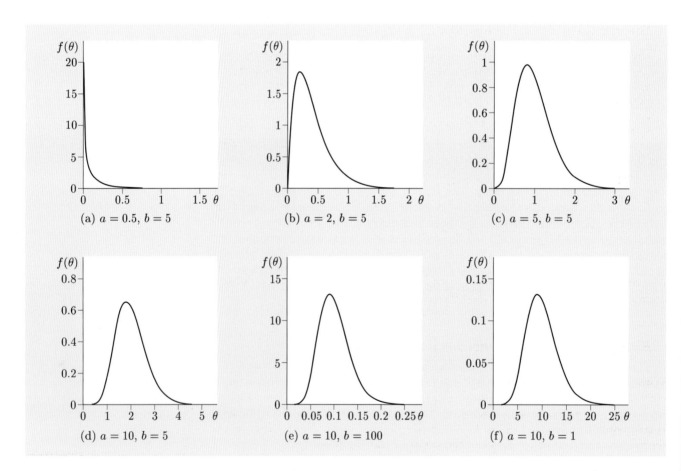

(a) $a = 0.5$, $b = 5$

(b) $a = 2$, $b = 5$

(c) $a = 5$, $b = 5$

(d) $a = 10$, $b = 5$

(e) $a = 10$, $b = 100$

(f) $a = 10$, $b = 1$

Figure 5.9 $\text{Gamma}(a, b)$ priors for various values of parameters a and b

The shape of the gamma prior is determined by the value of the parameter a, which is often referred to as the **shape parameter**. The gamma prior is positively skewed, but becomes less skewed as a becomes larger. This is illustrated in Figure 5.9: the values of the parameter a for the priors in Figures 5.9(a), 5.9(b), 5.9(c) and 5.9(d) are 0.5, 2, 5 and 10, respectively. For large a, the gamma prior is similar in shape to a normal prior.

The parameter b has no effect on the shape of the density. Notice that the priors in Figures 5.9(d), 5.9(e) and 5.9(f) all have the same shape — only the scales on the axes are different.

The gamma prior has a single mode. For $a > 1$, the mode is given by

$$\text{mode} = \frac{a-1}{b}. \tag{5.5}$$

For $a \leq 1$, the mode is at 0. Notice that the larger a is compared to b, the larger is the mode. For a given value of the mode, the peak in the prior density becomes more pronounced as b increases.

Activity 5.7   Shapes and modes of gamma priors

For which of the priors Gamma$(4, 1)$, Gamma$(4, 0.1)$, Gamma$(31, 1)$ and Gamma$(31, 0.1)$ is the mode the same? Which of the priors have the same shape?

A summary of the gamma prior is given in the following box.

The gamma prior Gamma(a, b)

The **gamma prior**, with parameters $a > 0$ and $b > 0$, which is denoted Gamma(a, b), may be used to represent prior beliefs about a parameter θ which takes only non-negative values. The parameter a is the **shape** parameter.

◇   When $a > 1$, the distribution has a single mode, given by

$$\text{mode} = \frac{a-1}{b}.$$

When $0 < a \leq 1$, there is a single mode at 0.

◇   The mean and variance of Gamma(a, b) are given by

$$\text{mean} = \frac{a}{b}, \quad \text{variance} = \frac{a}{b^2}.$$

A special use of the gamma prior is to represent prior beliefs about a parameter known as the *precision*. This is described in Example 5.9.

Example 5.9   A prior distribution for the precision

When dealing with a normal distribution $N(\mu, \sigma^2)$ in Bayesian statistics, it is common to work with the reciprocal of the variance, rather than the variance itself. The reciprocal of the variance, σ^{-2}, is called the **precision**. The precision is commonly denoted by τ. (The Greek letter τ is pronounced 'taw'.) Figure 5.10 represents the relationship between the variance and the precision.

When the variance increases, the precision decreases, and vice versa. The variance is always positive, so τ is also always positive. Consequently, a gamma prior may be a suitable prior for τ.

It might also be sensible to use a gamma prior for the variance σ^2. However, for reasons that will be discussed later, it is more common to use a gamma prior for the precision. ◆

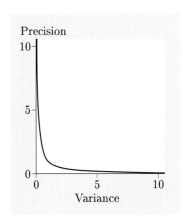

Figure 5.10   The relationship between variance and precision

The four standard priors — normal, uniform, beta and gamma — have now been introduced. An important skill in Bayesian statistics is to be able to specify an appropriate prior distribution. Activities 5.8 to 5.11 will give you some practice at choosing a suitable prior. All the parameters defined in these activities will be revisited in Sections 6 to 9.

Activity 5.8 Telephone calls and junk mail

In this part of Book 4, you will perform your own prior to posterior analysis to learn about two parameters personal to you. These are defined as follows:

θ_{phone} = mean number of telephone calls you receive each week,

θ_{junk} = probability that you receive two or more items of junk mail in a day.

The first stage in an analysis is to specify a prior. Which of the standard priors might be suitable for θ_{phone}? Which of the standard priors might be suitable for θ_{junk}? Briefly justify your answers. Keep a record of your answers as you will need them later.

You will learn how to specify values for the parameters of your priors in Section 6.

Activity 5.9 Paediatric cardiology

This activity concerns the problem of making an initial diagnosis of a heart problem in a very young baby, based on data reported over the telephone. The initial diagnosis is used to decide the best course of action for the baby while the baby is transferred to the specialist hospital. The doctor who is referring the baby for specialist treatment is asked 24 questions over the telephone. One such question is whether the baby has heart failure, with possible responses 'yes' and 'no'.

In one study, only babies with transposition of the great arteries were included. In this study, the parameter of interest is

$\theta = P$(baby with transposition of the great arteries has heart failure).

Identify two standard priors that could be used to represent beliefs about θ.

Spiegelhalter, D.J., Harris, N.L., Bull, K. and Franklin, R.C.G. (1994) Empirical evaluation of prior beliefs about frequencies: methodology and a case study in congenital heart disease. *Journal of the American Statistical Association*, **89**, 435–443.

Activity 5.10 Progression of Alzheimer's disease

In designing a trial of a new drug to slow the progression of Alzheimer's disease, it is of interest to learn about the natural progression of the disease in a particular population. This is assessed using an index that measures various aspects of short-term memory. Changes in this index over time determine the speed of progression of the disease. The parameter θ of interest is the mean change in the index value one year after diagnosis of Alzheimer's disease.

A negative value of θ indicates that, on average in this population, the condition worsens in the year after diagnosis; a positive value, on the other hand, indicates that, on average, there is an improvement.

Identify a standard prior that could be used to represent beliefs about θ.

Activity 5.11 Nuclear reactor plant failures

A commercial nuclear reactor plant contains a high pressure coolant injection (HPCI) system. A study was carried out to estimate the parameter θ, where θ is the failure rate of the HPCI system. (The failure rate is the average number of failures per reactor year.)

Which of the standard priors might be suitable for θ? Briefly justify your answer.

Martz, H.F. and Picard, R.R. (1995) Uncertainty in Poisson event counts and exposure time in rate estimation. *Reliability Engineering and System Safety*, **48**, 181–190.

Summary of Section 5

In this section, the idea of using a standard distribution as a prior has been introduced. Four families of standard priors have been discussed — the normal, uniform, beta and gamma families — each of which has two parameters denoted a and b. The situations in which each of these four distributions may be used as priors have been described. For each family of priors, you have seen how the shape of the prior varies with the values of the parameters a and b.

Exercise on Section 5

Exercise 5.1   Choosing a prior

In each of the situations described below, identify which (one or more) standard priors might be suitable to represent prior beliefs about θ. In each case, justify your choice.

(a) Health experts recommend that we should eat five or more portions of fruit and vegetables every day. Let θ be the proportion of children aged 5 to 15 years who eat five or more portions of fruit and vegetables every day.

(b) Domestic waste collectors are a high-risk occupational group with respect to health and safety. A study was carried out to estimate the parameter θ, where θ is the annual rate of musculoskeletal injuries amongst domestic waste collectors in Florida, USA.

Englehardt, J.D., An, H., Fleming, L.E. and Bean, J.A. (2003) Analytical predictive Bayesian assessment of occupational injury risk: Municipal solid waste collectors. *Risk Analysis*, **23**, 917–927.

6   Specifying the prior

Suppose that you wish to represent your prior beliefs about some parameter θ using one of the standard distributions described in Section 5. Once you have decided which one of the standard families of priors to use — $N(a, b)$, $U(a, b)$, Beta(a, b) or Gamma(a, b) — the next step is to specify values for the parameters a and b, so that the density reflects your opinions about θ. Choosing the parameters a and b to reflect your opinions is the topic of this section.

For the uniform distribution $U(a, b)$, the values a and b are determined entirely by the range of values of θ that you believe are possible. For the other three standard families, $N(a, b)$, Beta(a, b) and Gamma(a, b), there are three steps to choosing the values of the parameters a and b. These steps are given in the following box.

Specifying the prior $f(\theta)$

◇   Assess the location of $f(\theta)$.

◇   Assess the spread of $f(\theta)$.

◇   Calculate the values of a and b that give the assessed location and spread.

Assessing the location is described in Subsection 6.1, and assessing the spread in Subsection 6.2. The calculation of a and b for normal distributions is described in Subsection 6.3. The method for beta and gamma distributions is also discussed briefly. In practice, it is easier to use computer software to calculate the values of a and b; you will use *LearnBayes* to do this in Section 7.

6.1   Assessing the location of the prior

Three measures which can be used to summarize the location (or average value) of a prior distribution for a parameter θ are the mode, the median and the mean. They are defined as follows.

These measures of location are described in the Introduction to statistical modelling.

◇   The **mode** is the value of θ where the maximum value of $f(\theta)$ occurs. So the mode is the most likely value of θ.

◇   The **median** is the value of θ which cuts the area under the prior density $f(\theta)$ into two in such a way that 50% of the area lies to the left of the median and 50% to the right.

◇   The **mean** is the average or expected value of θ.

For a symmetric density, the mode, the median and the mean coincide. This is illustrated in Figure 6.1(a).

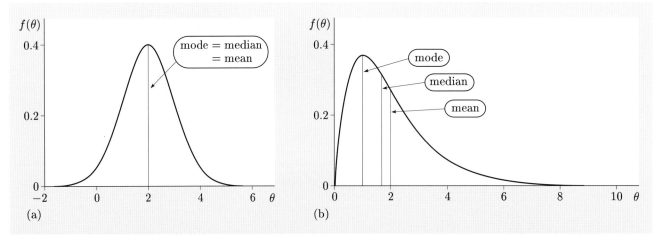

Figure 6.1   Two prior densities: (a) symmetric (b) right-skew

However, this is not the case for prior densities such as the beta and gamma densities which are skewed. Figure 6.1(b) shows a distribution that is positively skewed: the mode, median and mean are all different. In practice, it is difficult to specify the mean of a skew distribution. On the other hand, the mode and median are more easily assessed. Moreover, psychological research suggests that using either of these measures leads to priors which reflect the true opinions about the location of θ fairly well.

Skewness is defined in Section 2 of the Introduction to statistical modelling.

Assessing the mode is particularly straightforward: the mode of the prior density $f(\theta)$ is simply the value of θ which you believe to be the most likely.

Example 6.1   Assessed mode for nuclear reactor plant failure rate

Activity 5.11 concerned a commercial nuclear reactor containing a high pressure coolant injection (HPCI) system. The parameter θ is the failure rate of the HPCI system (that is, the average number of failures per reactor year). Based on expert advice, the most likely value for θ was assessed to be 0.77. Thus the location of the mode of a prior for θ based on this expert advice is 0.77.   ◆

Activity 6.1   Trust in politicians

An opinion poll which was carried out to estimate θ, the proportion of adults in Great Britain who trust politicians to tell the truth, was described in Example 3.2. What value for θ do *you* believe to be the most likely? Hence assess the mode of your prior for θ.

Note that you are asked to assess not your own opinion about whether or not politicians can be trusted to tell the truth, but what you believe to be the proportion of adults who trust politicians to tell the truth.

Activity 6.2   Assessed modes for θ_{phone} and θ_{junk}

In Activity 5.8, you chose families of prior distributions to represent your prior beliefs about two parameters that are personal to you, θ_{phone} and θ_{junk}:

θ_{phone} = mean number of telephone calls you receive each week,   *at 20*

θ_{junk} = probability that you receive two or more items of junk mail in a day.   *0.1*

Specify the values that you believe are the most likely for the parameters. Hence assess the modes of your prior distributions for θ_{phone} and θ_{junk}. Keep a record of your answers.

Assessing the location of a prior distribution using the mode works only if there is a most likely value. A situation in which there may be no single most likely value is described in Example 6.2.

Example 6.2   Waiting for Godot

Suppose that a furniture store has told you that the new piece of furniture you have bought will be delivered between 1 pm and 5 pm this afternoon. When pressed, the delivery staff cannot be more explicit. At 2 pm, the delivery has not yet been made, and you wonder how much longer you will have to wait. You believe that the delivery is equally likely to arrive at any time between 2 pm and 5 pm. Hence your prior distribution for the further time you will wait is flat, so it has no mode.   ◆

Assessing the median of your prior provides an alternative way of summarizing the location of the prior. How this might be done is illustrated in Example 6.3.

Example 6.3   Distance from Plymouth to Norwich

Andrew (a student in Norwich) was asked to consider θ, the distance in miles (by road) from Plymouth to Norwich, and to give his assessment of the distance. His assessed value was 240 miles. After giving this assessment, he was asked which of the following two options was more likely.

◇   The true distance is greater than 240 miles.

◇   The true distance is less than 240 miles.

He said that he believed that the two were equally likely. In other words, $P(\theta > 240) = P(\theta < 240) = \frac{1}{2}$. Therefore 240 (miles) is his assessed median of the prior for θ.   ◆

Activity 6.3   Distance from Plymouth to Norwich: your beliefs

Is your opinion about the distance from Plymouth to Norwich the same as Andrew's? If it is, then your assessed value of the median m of your prior for θ is 240 miles. If your opinion differs from Andrew's, then which of statements A and B below do you believe to be the more likely?

A: The distance from Plymouth to Norwich is more than 240 miles.

B: The distance from Plymouth to Norwich is less than 240 miles.

If you believe that A is more likely than B, then change 240 miles to some larger value m. If you believe that B is more likely than A, then change 240 miles to some smaller value m. In either case, decide which of statements A' and B' overleaf you believe to be more likely.

A': The distance from Plymouth to Norwich is greater than m.

B': The distance from Plymouth to Norwich is less than m.

Continue adjusting the value of m in this way until you reach a value m that satisfies $P(\theta > m) = P(\theta < m) = \frac{1}{2}$. This is then *your* assessment of the median for *your* prior.

Estimating the median requires making judgements about whether two probabilities are equal. Psychological research suggests that this yields more accurate results than, say, judging whether one probability is five times larger than another. For this reason, the median is generally estimated fairly well. However, the mode is often easier to work with, so the mode will generally be used to assess the location of the prior in this book.

6.2   Assessing the spread of the prior

The spread of the prior reflects the uncertainty in your prior beliefs about θ: the less certain you are about the value of θ, the greater will be the spread of your prior $f(\theta)$. The variance and the standard deviation of the distribution are commonly used measures of spread. However, it is usually very difficult to assess the variance or the standard deviation of the prior for θ directly. Thus other approaches to assessing the spread must be used. One of the most common approaches is to specify a probability $1 - \alpha$, and assess an interval (L, U) such that

$$P(L < \theta \le U) = 1 - \alpha.$$

It is usual to focus on the central part of the prior so that

$$P(\theta \le L) = P(\theta > U) = \tfrac{1}{2}\alpha.$$

Thus L is the $\alpha/2$-quantile and U is the $(1 - \alpha/2)$-quantile of the prior for θ. The interval (L, U) is called the **equal-tailed $100(1 - \alpha)\%$ interval**.

Equal-tailed intervals provide a measure of the spread of the prior: the wider the interval (L, U), the greater is the spread of the prior.

Equal-tailed intervals are also called **central** intervals.

Example 6.4   Distance from Plymouth to Norwich: Andrew's opinion

Andrew gave his assessment of the median of his prior for the distance from Plymouth to Norwich as 240 miles. He was then asked to estimate an equal-tailed interval (L, U) for his prior for θ which he believed to contain the central 50% of his prior. Andrew chose the values $L = 220$ miles and $U = 260$ miles. Thus $(220, 260)$ miles is the assessed interval containing the central 50% of his prior:

See Example 6.3.

$$P(L < \theta \le U) = P(220 < \theta \le 260) = 1 - \alpha = 0.5.$$

Moreover, as this interval gives the central 50% of his prior, 220 is his assessed value of $q_{0.25}$ (the lower quartile of his prior) and 260 is his assessed value of $q_{0.75}$ (the upper quartile).   ◆

Activity 6.4   Distance from Plymouth to Norwich: Lucy's opinion

Lucy, who is also a student in Norwich, gives an interval which she believes to contain the central 50% of her prior for θ. Lucy's assessed interval is $(185, 275)$ miles. Who is the more confident in their assessment of the distance from Plymouth to Norwich, Andrew or Lucy? Explain your answer.

For a 50% equal-tailed interval, the value of α is 0.5. Other values of α can be used, as illustrated in Activity 6.5.

Activity 6.5   Assessing the nuclear reactor plant failure rate

Activity 5.11 concerned a study to evaluate the performance of the high pressure coolant injection (HPCI) system of a commercial nuclear reactor. The parameter of interest is

θ = failure rate of the HPCI system.

The equal-tailed interval $(0.55, 1.39)$ was judged to contain the middle 66% (roughly two-thirds) of the prior for θ. Which quantiles of the prior for θ are the values 0.55 and 1.39?

The equal-tailed intervals in Example 6.4 and Activity 6.5 were 50% and 66% intervals, so the values of α used were 0.5 and 0.34, respectively. Smaller values of α are sometimes used — for example, $\alpha = 0.1$ or $\alpha = 0.05$. For small α, the interval (L, U) represents the range of most likely values of θ. However, studies have shown that people tend to be over-confident about their beliefs, and often give insufficient probability to the tails of the distribution. Therefore subjectively assessed equal-tailed intervals with small α, and hence large $1 - \alpha$, may be inaccurate.

Assessing the spread of the prior is summarized in the following box.

Assessing the spread of the prior

To assess the spread of the prior for a parameter θ, an **equal-tailed** $100(1 - \alpha)\%$ **interval** (L, U) is obtained, where L is the $\alpha/2$-quantile and U is the $(1 - \alpha/2)$-quantile of the prior.

Commonly used values of $1 - \alpha$ are 0.5, in which case L and U are the lower and upper quartiles of the prior for θ, and 0.66.

Activity 6.6   Assessed intervals for θ_{phone} and θ_{junk}

In Activity 6.2, you assessed the modes of your prior distributions for the parameters θ_{phone} and θ_{junk}. Assess the lower quartile L and the upper quartile U of your prior distribution for each of the parameters. Hence obtain an equal-tailed 50% interval for each of your prior distributions. Keep a record of your answers.

Once you have completed Activity 6.6 you will be ready to obtain the priors for θ_{phone} and θ_{junk}. You will use *LearnBayes* to do this in Section 7.

In Section 9, you will need data on the number of phone calls you receive and on the number of items of junk mail you receive. These data will take one week to collect. The data you should collect are described in Activity 6.7.

Activity 6.7   *Collect data*

(a) Each day over the next week, record the number of telephone calls you receive. At the end of the week, add the numbers of calls received on the seven days to obtain the total number of telephone calls you received in the week.

(b) Each day over the next week (but not on Sunday), record whether or not you receive two or more items of junk mail. At the end of the week, count the total number of days (out of six) on which you received two or more items of junk mail.

Start collecting these data now.

6.3   *Determining parameters for standard priors*

Assessing the location and spread of a prior has been discussed in Subsections 6.1 and 6.2. The final step in specifying a standard prior — $N(a, b)$, $\text{Beta}(a, b)$, $\text{Gamma}(a, b)$ or $U(a, b)$ — is to find values of the parameters a and b such that the location and spread of the prior match the assessed location and spread. A perfect match is not always possible. However, an approximate match is usually good enough. Calculating the values of the parameters a and b which match the assessed location and spread is described in this subsection for each of the four standard families of priors.

Uniform priors

When the prior is uniform $U(a, b)$, the parameters a and b are determined entirely by the range of values of θ that are believed to be possible: a is the minimum possible value and b is the maximum possible value.

Example 6.5   *Waiting for Godot, continued*

In Example 6.2, the situation where you are waiting for the delivery of a new piece of furniture was described. At 2 pm, the parameter θ is the further time that you will have to wait. Since you think that the delivery is equally likely to arrive at any time between now (2 pm) and 5 pm, you have chosen a uniform prior $U(a, b)$. The minimum value of θ is 0, and the maximum value (in minutes) is 180. Thus $a = 0$ and $b = 180$.   ◆

Normal priors

The median, mode and mean of the normal distribution $N(a, b)$ are all equal to a. Hence a should be your assessed value of the mode (or median) of the prior for θ.

To obtain b, suppose that L is the assessed $\alpha/2$-quantile and U is the assessed $(1 - \alpha/2)$-quantile of the prior for θ. Then the quantiles L and U can be used to obtain the corresponding value of the variance b, as follows. If $X \sim N(\mu, \sigma^2)$, then $(X - \mu)/\sigma \sim N(0, 1)$. Hence, if $\theta \sim N(a, b)$, then

$$\frac{\theta - a}{\sqrt{b}} \sim N(0, 1).$$

Therefore

$$\frac{L - a}{\sqrt{b}} = q_{\alpha/2}, \qquad \frac{U - a}{\sqrt{b}} = q_{1-\alpha/2},$$

where $q_{\alpha/2}$ is the $\alpha/2$-quantile and $q_{1-\alpha/2}$ is the $(1 - \alpha/2)$-quantile of $N(0,1)$.

Now if z is the $(1 - \alpha/2)$-quantile of $N(0,1)$, then $-z$ is the $\alpha/2$-quantile. Hence

$$\frac{L - a}{\sqrt{b}} = -z, \qquad \frac{U - a}{\sqrt{b}} = z.$$

A table of quantiles of the standard normal distribution is given in the *Handbook*.

Subtracting the equation on the left from that on the right gives

$$\frac{U - L}{\sqrt{b}} = 2z.$$

Rearranging this equation gives the following expression for b:

$$b = \left(\frac{U - L}{2z}\right)^2.$$

Specifying the parameters of a normal prior is summarized in the following box.

Specifying a normal prior $N(a, b)$

The mean a and variance b of a normal prior may be assessed as follows:

$$a = \text{assessed mode or median,}$$

$$b = \left(\frac{U - L}{2z}\right)^2, \tag{6.1}$$

where L is the assessed $\alpha/2$-quantile and U is the assessed $(1 - \alpha/2)$-quantile of the prior for θ, and z is the $(1 - \alpha/2)$-quantile of $N(0,1)$.

Example 6.6   Weather forecasting

Meteorologists are increasingly required to attach probabilities to their forecasts. Suppose that the quantity of interest is the predicted temperature at noon tomorrow, denoted θ. A normal prior for θ is a reasonable choice.

One meteorologist's assessment of the mode of the prior for θ is 15°C. His assessment for a is therefore 15.

Suppose that he is asked to assess the equal-tailed 50% interval (L, U), so that L and U are the lower and upper quartiles of the prior for θ, and that his assessments are $L = 13$°C and $U = 17$°C. Here $1 - \alpha = 0.5$, so $1 - \alpha/2 = 0.75$, and hence z is the upper quartile of $N(0,1)$. From tables, the 0.75-quantile z of $N(0,1)$ is 0.6745. Hence, using Formula (6.1), the value of b which matches the assessed values of L and U is given by

$$b = \left(\frac{U - L}{2z}\right)^2 = \left(\frac{17 - 13}{2 \times 0.6745}\right)^2 \simeq 8.79.$$

The meteorologist's assessed prior is therefore $N(15, 8.79)$.   ♦

Note that, for a normal prior, the assessed interval (L, U) should be symmetric about the assessed value of a. In practice, this might not be the case. However, as long as the asymmetry is not too serious, then it is usually reasonable to approximate the prior by a normal distribution, using the assessed mode or median for a, and using Formula (6.1) to calculate a value for b.

Example 6.7   Weather forecasting, continued

A second meteorologist was asked to specify a prior for θ. Suppose that this second meteorologist also assesses a to be 15, but is asked to assess the interval (L, U) which contains the middle 66% (roughly two-thirds) of the prior. Suppose that her assessed values are $L = 12.5°\mathrm{C}$ and $U = 17°\mathrm{C}$. Note that the interval (L, U) is not symmetric about $a = 15$. However, since it is not very asymmetric, it is not unreasonable to use a normal prior. In this case, $1 - \alpha = 0.66$, so $1 - \alpha/2 = 0.83$ and hence z is the 0.83-quantile of $N(0, 1)$. From tables, the 0.83-quantile of $N(0, 1)$ is 0.9542. Hence, using Formula (6.1),

$$b = \left(\frac{U - L}{2z} \right)^2 = \left(\frac{17 - 12.5}{2 \times 0.9542} \right)^2 \simeq 5.56.$$

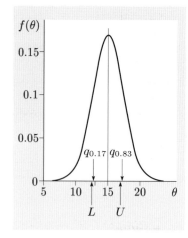

Figure 6.2   The second meteorologist's prior, $N(15, 5.56)$

Therefore the assessed prior is $N(15, 5.56)$. Notice that although the interval (L, U) is wider than that chosen by the meteorologist in Example 6.6, the value of b is smaller because the value of $1 - \alpha$ that was used is larger.

A plot of the second meteorologist's prior is shown in Figure 6.2.

The 0.17-quantile and the 0.83-quantile of the prior $N(15, 5.56)$ are also shown on Figure 6.2, together with the corresponding assessed quantiles L and U. As you can see, the assessed quantiles do not differ much from the quantiles of the normal prior.   ◆

Activities 6.8 and 6.9 will give you some practice at specifying normal priors.

Activity 6.8   A prior for the distance from Plymouth to Norwich

In Example 6.4, Andrew's assessed value of the median of the prior for the distance from Plymouth to Norwich was 240 miles, and his assessed values for the lower and upper quartiles were 220 and 260 miles, respectively. Use these values to calculate values for the parameters a and b for a normal prior, and hence specify the normal prior which represents Andrew's prior beliefs.

Activity 6.9   A prior for memory test improvement

In Example 5.2, θ was defined to be the average improvement on a memory test of temporal lobe epilepsy patients who do not have surgery. The neuropsychologist assesses that the most likely value of θ is 10; his assessed lower and upper quartiles for θ are 5 and 15, respectively. These quartiles are located symmetrically on either side of the mode, suggesting that the neuropsychologist's prior opinions about θ can be represented by a symmetric probability distribution. Therefore it seems reasonable to represent his opinions by a normal distribution.

Use the assessed values to specify a normal prior representing the neuropsychologist's opinions about θ.

Beta priors and gamma priors

Methods similar to those for the normal distribution may be used to determine the parameters a and b of $\mathrm{Beta}(a, b)$ and $\mathrm{Gamma}(a, b)$ distributions. However, tables of beta and gamma distributions are not usually readily available. In Section 7, given assessments of the mode and an equal-tailed $100(1 - \alpha)\%$ interval (L, U), you will use *LearnBayes* to estimate a and b for a beta distribution and a gamma distribution. As for the normal distribution, there is often no combination of a and b that will produce a distribution that exactly matches the assessments. However, it is usually possible to obtain values of a and b that give a close match.

Example 6.8   Arthritis drug

A medical researcher was questioned about the proportion of arthritis sufferers who would be helped by a new drug. Let θ denote this proportion. Since θ is a proportion, a beta distribution is a reasonable choice of prior for θ. The researcher was first asked to specify the median of the prior for θ. He was of the opinion that the probability that θ exceeded 0.4 was equal to the probability that θ was below 0.4. Hence 0.4 is his assessed median. Upon further questioning, he also gave $L = 0.3$ and $U = 0.5$ as his assessed lower and upper quartiles for the prior for θ. The median of a beta distribution with parameters $a = 4$ and $b = 6$ is 0.393, the lower quartile is 0.291 and upper quartile is 0.502. These values are close to the researcher's assessments, so it is reasonable to represent his opinions by a Beta$(4, 6)$ distribution.   ♦

The median and quartiles of Beta$(4, 6)$ were found using *LearnBayes*.

Example 6.9   Junk email

When Jane arrives at work she usually finds junk email messages in her computer mailbox. Let θ be the average number of junk email messages received per day (excluding Mondays).

Since the parameter θ is positive, a gamma prior may be appropriate for θ. Suppose that Jane's assessment of the most likely number of junk emails she receives per day is 3, and that the interval $(2, 6)$ contains the central 66% of her prior for θ. That is, for her assessed prior, $L = q_{0.17} = 2$ and $U = q_{0.83} = 6$. A gamma distribution with $a = 4$ and $b = 1$ has mode 3.00, $q_{0.17} = 2.15$ and $q_{0.83} = 5.80$. These are close to Jane's assessed quantiles, so it seems reasonable to take Gamma$(4, 1)$ as Jane's prior.   ♦

Mondays are excluded because junk email usually accumulates over the weekend, so the average number of junk email messages on Mondays is different from that on other days of the week.

The mode and quantiles of Gamma$(4, 1)$ were found using *LearnBayes*.

As illustrated in Example 6.9, finding a prior that matches the assessed mode (or median) and the assessed quantiles L and U involves some juggling. This is illustrated in Activity 6.10.

Activity 6.10   Modes of beta distributions

Suppose that θ has a Beta(a, b) distribution and that the assessed mode of θ is 0.2.

(a) (i)   If a is chosen to be 5, what value of b would give this mode?

    (ii)   If b is chosen to be 16, what value of a would give this mode?

(b) Suppose that the assessed mode and the assessed value of the lower quartile L give the estimate $a = 5$, while the assessed mode and the assessed value of the upper quartile U give the estimate $b = 16$. Suggest a beta distribution to use as the assessor's prior. (*Hint*: find the averages of the values given here for a and b and the values which you obtained in part (a) for a and b, and check that the mode is close to 0.2 for the average values of a and b.)

Summary of Section 6

In this section, assessing the location and spread of a prior has been discussed. The location has been assessed using the mode and the median. The spread has been assessed using an equal-tailed $100(1 - \alpha)\%$ interval (L, U), where L and U are the assessed $\alpha/2$-quantile and the assessed $(1 - \alpha/2)$-quantile of the prior, respectively. The recommended values of $1 - \alpha$ to use are 0.5 and 0.66. A method for calculating the parameters of a normal prior from assessed values of the location and spread has been described. Calculating the parameters of beta priors and gamma priors has also been discussed briefly.

Exercises on Section 6

Exercise 6.1   Another prior for the distance from Plymouth to Norwich

Lucy assessed that the interval $(185, 275)$ contains the central 50% of her prior for θ, the distance (in miles) from Plymouth to Norwich. Suppose that her assessed median is 235 miles. Find a normal prior which represents her beliefs about θ.

See Activity 6.4.

Exercise 6.2   Modes for beta priors

Suppose that the parameter θ is a proportion and that a beta prior $\text{Beta}(a, b)$ is to be used to represent prior beliefs about θ. The mode for θ has been assessed to be 0.65.

(a) If the parameter a is chosen to be 10, what value of b gives a beta prior with mode 0.65?

(b) If the parameter b is chosen to be 10, what value of a gives a beta prior with mode 0.65?

(c) Which of the priors in parts (a) and (b) represents stronger beliefs about θ?

Exercise 6.3   Modes for gamma priors

Suppose that the parameter θ is positive and that a gamma prior $\text{Gamma}(a, b)$ is to be used to represent prior beliefs about θ. The mode for θ has been assessed to be 4.

(a) If the parameter a is chosen to be 7, what value of b gives a gamma prior with mode 4?

(b) If the parameter b is chosen to be 2, what value of a gives a gamma prior with mode 4?

(c) Suppose that the assessed mode and the quantile L give an estimate of 7 for a, while the assessed mode and the quantile U give an estimate of 2 for b. Suggest a gamma distribution to use as the prior for θ.

7   Exploring normal, beta and gamma priors

In this section, you will use *LearnBayes* to explore the standard prior distributions that were introduced in Section 5. You will investigate how the shape of the prior changes when the parameter values are changed. Assessing the location and spread of a prior was discussed in Section 6. You learned how to calculate the values of the parameters a and b for a normal prior using the assessed location and spread. Calculating a and b for beta and gamma priors was also discussed briefly. In this section, you will use *LearnBayes* to calculate the values of a and b for normal, beta and gamma priors.

Refer to Chapter 3 of Computer Book 4 for the work in this section.

Summary of Section 7

In this section, you have used *LearnBayes* to explore normal, beta and gamma priors, and to find the prior which is the best match for given assessments of the prior mode and quantiles.

8 Conjugate analyses

Specifying the prior distribution for a parameter θ has been discussed in Sections 5 and 6. The prior represents beliefs about θ before any data are obtained. Now suppose that some data are collected, which provide information about θ. This information is summarized by the likelihood function $L(\theta)$. In Section 3, you saw that the likelihood and the prior distribution are combined to form the posterior distribution:

posterior $\propto$ likelihood $\times$ prior,

or, equivalently,

posterior $= k \times$ likelihood $\times$ prior, $\hspace{2cm}$ (8.1)

where k is a constant, not involving θ, which ensures that the area under the posterior distribution is equal to 1.

In practice, it may be difficult to calculate the constant k. However, for some likelihoods, a prior can be used which produces a posterior distribution of the same form as the prior distribution. In this case, the posterior distribution can be identified from its form, so the constant k does not need to be calculated. Such a prior is called a **conjugate prior**. When a conjugate prior is used, the prior to posterior Bayesian analysis is called a **conjugate analysis**.

In this context, the term 'conjugate' means 'fits together'.

Conjugate analyses are described in this section — for a proportion in Subsection 8.1, for the mean of a Poisson distribution in Subsection 8.2, and for the mean of a normal distribution in Subsection 8.3. The use of uniform priors is discussed in Subsection 8.4. In Subsection 8.5, you will use *LearnBayes* to carry out conjugate analyses.

8.1 Conjugate analysis for a proportion

In this subsection, the parameter θ of interest is a proportion. The standard prior for a proportion is a beta distribution. The conjugate analysis in this case is illustrated in Example 8.1.

Example 8.1 Conjugate analysis for trust in politicians

In Example 3.2, the parameter θ was defined to be the proportion of individuals who trust politicians to tell the truth. The standard prior for a proportion is a beta distribution. The density of a beta prior for a parameter θ has the form

$$f(\theta) = c \times \theta^{a-1}(1-\theta)^{b-1},$$ $\hspace{2cm}$ (8.2)

The density of a beta prior is given in Formula (5.2).

for some choice of a and b (both greater than 0).

Now suppose that a sample of 50 adults in Great Britain are asked whether they trust politicians to tell the truth. Let X denote the number who answer 'yes'. A reasonable model for X is the binomial distribution $B(50, \theta)$. In this case, the probability mass function for X is

$$p(x|\theta) = \binom{50}{x} \theta^x (1-\theta)^{50-x}.$$

Suppose that in the sample collected, $X = 11$ individuals replied 'yes'. Then the likelihood of θ for this sample of size 50 is given by

$$L(\theta) = \binom{50}{11} \theta^{11}(1-\theta)^{39}.$$

The posterior for θ is calculated using (8.1):

$$f(\theta|X = 11) = k \times \binom{50}{11} \theta^{11}(1 - \theta)^{39} \times c \times \theta^{a-1}(1 - \theta)^{b-1}$$
$$= c^* \times \theta^{11+a-1}(1 - \theta)^{39+b-1},$$

where

$$c^* = k \times \binom{50}{11} \times c.$$

The constant c^* ensures that the area under the posterior distribution is equal to 1. Notice that $f(\theta|X = 11)$ has the same form as the beta prior in (8.2), but with parameter $11 + a$ instead of a, and parameter $39 + b$ instead of b. The posterior distribution for θ, given that $X = 11$, is therefore a beta distribution. Consequently, since the posterior is known to be $\text{Beta}(11 + a, 39 + b)$, there is no need to calculate the constant c^* to specify the posterior fully. For example, if the prior for θ is the beta distribution with $a = 10$ and $b = 20$, then the posterior distribution is beta with parameters $11 + 10 = 21$ and $39 + 20 = 59$.   ◆

More generally, suppose that θ is a proportion, and that the prior distribution for θ is $\text{Beta}(a, b)$. If the data x are binomial $B(n, \theta)$, then the likelihood of θ is of the form

$$L(\theta) = \text{constant} \times \theta^x(1 - \theta)^{n-x}.$$

Then, using an argument similar to that in Example 8.1, it can be shown that the posterior distribution for θ, given x, is the beta distribution $\text{Beta}(a + x, b + n - x)$. This model is called the **beta/binomial model**. It is summarized in the following box.

The beta/binomial model

Suppose that θ is a proportion, with beta prior distribution with parameters a and b:

$$\theta \sim \text{Beta}(a, b).$$

Suppose that X may be modelled by the binomial distribution $B(n, \theta)$:

$$X \sim B(n, \theta).$$

If data $X = x$ are collected, then the posterior distribution for θ, given x, is beta with parameters $a + x$ and $b + n - x$:

$$\theta|\text{data} \sim \text{Beta}(a + x, b + n - x). \tag{8.3}$$

The notation $\theta|\text{data}$ indicates that the given distribution is the posterior for θ.

Activity 8.1   Posteriors for trust in politicians

(a) Verify that the posterior for θ in Example 8.1 is of the form $\text{Beta}(a + x, b + n - x)$.

(b) The following beta priors for θ were among those used in Example 3.2 and Activity 3.2: $\text{Beta}(5, 7)$, $\text{Beta}(60, 90)$, $\text{Beta}(5, 2)$ and $\text{Beta}(110, 28)$. For each of these priors, find the posterior distribution for θ after observing $X = 11$ from $B(50, \theta)$.

For the beta prior, the value of $a + b$ increases as the strength of the prior beliefs about θ increase. Similarly, for the beta posterior, the value $(a + x) + (b + n - x) = a + b + n$ represents the strength of the posterior beliefs about θ, that is, the beliefs after the data have been observed. Note that since $a + b + n > a + b$, observing data always increases the strength of the beliefs about θ. The larger the value of n, the larger is the relative contribution of the data to the strength of the posterior beliefs. Similarly, the larger the value of $a + b$, the larger is the relative contribution of the prior beliefs.

The strength of beta priors was discussed in Subsection 5.3.

Example 8.2   Strength of beliefs

In Activity 8.1, you found that with the relatively weak prior Beta$(5, 2)$, the posterior distribution is Beta$(16, 41)$. In this case, $a + b = 5 + 2 = 7$ and $n = 50$, so $a + b$ is much smaller than n, and hence the prior contributes less to the posterior than the data. The posterior distribution is closer to the likelihood than to the prior, as shown in Figure 8.1(a).

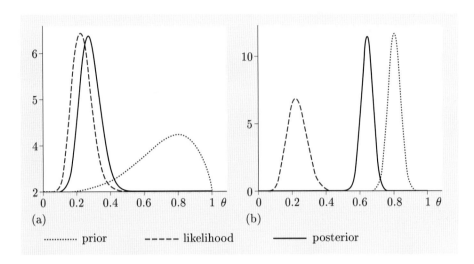

(a)

(b)

················ prior   ----- likelihood   ——— posterior

Figure 8.1   Prior, likelihood and posterior: (a) with Beta$(5, 2)$ prior (b) with Beta$(110, 28)$ prior

In contrast, for the stronger prior Beta$(110, 28)$, the prior contributes more to the posterior than the data: $a + b = 110 + 28 = 138$, which is greater than $n = 50$. In this case, the posterior distribution is closer to the prior than to the likelihood, as shown in Figure 8.1(b).   ◆

Activity 8.2   Posteriors for paediatric cardiology

The problem of diagnosing heart failure in a baby, given information provided over the telephone, was considered in Activity 5.9. The parameter of interest is θ, the probability that a baby with transposition of the great arteries has heart failure.

Suppose that it has been decided to represent prior beliefs about θ with the Beta$(1.42, 5.13)$ distribution. Of 58 babies observed with transposition of the great arteries, five were observed to have heart failure.

(a)   Calculate the posterior distribution for θ, given these data.

(b)   Discuss the relative contribution of the prior and the likelihood to the posterior distribution. Would you expect the posterior to be closer to the prior or to the likelihood? Explain your answer.

8.2 Conjugate analysis for a Poisson mean

In this subsection, conjugate analyses for a Poisson mean are considered. A Poisson random variable can take the values $0, 1, 2, \ldots$, so a Poisson mean cannot be negative. Therefore the gamma distribution might be an appropriate prior distribution. It can be shown that with this prior, the posterior distribution is also a gamma distribution. The conjugate analysis for a Poisson mean is described in Example 8.3.

The Poisson distribution is discussed in the Introduction to statistical modelling.

Example 8.3   Conjugate analysis for botulism intoxication

Botulism intoxication is a serious illness caused by the bacterium *Clostridium botulinum*. Foodborne botulism results from ingestion of contaminated food, particularly tinned food, and can be fatal. In England and Wales, foodborne botulism is very rare. The number of cases occurring each year can be modelled by a Poisson distribution with mean μ.

Suppose that prior beliefs about μ are represented by a gamma distribution with parameters a and b. Then the prior density is

$$f(\mu) = c \times \mu^{a-1} \exp(-b\mu),$$

The density of a gamma prior is given in Formula (5.4).

where c is a constant not involving μ.

Table 8.1 contains data on the number of cases of foodborne botulism in England and Wales in the eight years from 1998 to 2005.

These data were obtained in April 2006 from the website of the Health Protection Agency http://www.hpa.org.uk.

Table 8.1   Number of cases of foodborne botulism in England and Wales, 1998–2005

Year	1998	1999	2000	2001	2002	2003	2004	2005
Cases	2	0	0	0	1	0	2	1

Let X represent the number of cases of botulism in one year, so that $X \sim \text{Poisson}(\mu)$. The probability mass function for a single Poisson observation x is

$$p(x|\mu) = \frac{1}{x!}\mu^x \exp(-\mu).$$

For n independent observations $x_1, \ldots, x_n$ on X, the probability $p(\text{data}|\mu)$ is obtained by multiplying the probabilities $p(x_i|\mu)$ for the n observations. This leads to

See Subsection 3.3.

$$p(\text{data}|\mu) = \frac{1}{x_1! \cdots x_n!}\mu^{n\bar{x}} \exp(-n\mu),$$

where $\bar{x}$ is the mean of the n observations. For the botulism data, $n = 8$ and $\bar{x} = 6/8 = 0.75$. Thus the likelihood for μ, given the data, is

$$L(\mu) = c_1 \times \mu^6 \exp(-8\mu),$$

where c_1 is a constant not involving μ. The posterior distribution for μ, given the data, is obtained using (8.1):

$$\begin{aligned} f(\mu|\text{data}) &= k \times c_1 \times \mu^6 \exp(-8\mu) \times c \times \mu^{a-1} \exp(-b\mu) \\ &= c^* \times \mu^{a+5} \exp(-(b+8)\mu), \end{aligned}$$

where the constant c^* ensures that the area under the posterior distribution is 1. The posterior distribution is therefore a gamma distribution with parameters $a + 6$ and $b + 8$. Thus, for example, if the prior is gamma with $a = 1.5$ and $b = 0.5$, then the posterior for μ, given the data, is Gamma$(7.5, 8.5)$.   ◆

More generally, suppose that μ is a Poisson mean, and that the prior distribution for μ is Gamma(a, b). Then the posterior distribution for μ, given n observations from Poisson(μ) with sample mean $\bar{x}$, is the gamma distribution Gamma$(a + n\bar{x}, b + n)$. This model, which is often called the **gamma/Poisson model**, is summarized in the following box.

The gamma/Poisson model

Suppose that μ is a Poisson mean, and that the prior distribution for μ is gamma with parameters a and b:

$$\mu \sim \text{Gamma}(a, b).$$

Suppose that n observations with mean $\bar{x}$ are made on X, where

$$X \sim \text{Poisson}(\mu).$$

Then the posterior distribution for μ, given the data, is gamma with parameters $a + n\bar{x}$ and $b + n$:

$$\mu|\text{data} \sim \text{Gamma}(a + n\bar{x}, b + n). \tag{8.4}$$

Activity 8.3   Posterior for nuclear reactor failure rate

Activity 5.11 concerned a study to evaluate the performance of the high pressure coolant injection (HPCI) system of a commercial nuclear reactor. A prior for the parameter θ, the failure rate of the HPCI system, is Gamma$(4.7, 4.8)$. Suppose that the number of failures of the HPCI system was recorded for each of four years, with the results shown in Table 8.2.

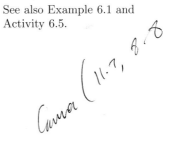

See also Example 6.1 and Activity 6.5.

Table 8.2   Number of failures of the HPCI system

Year	1	2	3	4
Number of failures	2	1	3	1

(a) Calculate the posterior for parameter θ, given these data.

(b) Figure 8.2 shows the prior, the likelihood and the posterior.

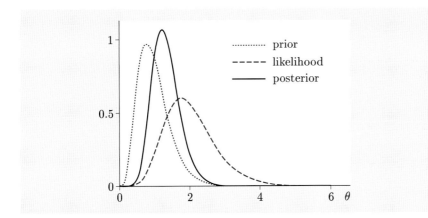

Figure 8.2   Prior, likelihood and posterior for reactor failure rate

On the basis of this diagram, say whether the posterior mode is closer to the likelihood mode or to the prior mode, and hence evaluate the relative contributions of the prior and the data to the posterior.

8.3   Conjugate analysis for a normal mean

In this subsection, conjugate analyses for a normal mean are described. Suppose that $X \sim N(\mu, \sigma^2)$, where σ^2 is known, and that a normal prior $N(a, b)$ has been chosen for μ. Given n observations $x_1, \ldots, x_n$ on X, it can be shown that the posterior for μ, given the data, is also a normal distribution. Since the prior and posterior are of the same form, the normal prior is conjugate to the normal likelihood for μ. This model is often referred to as the **normal/normal model**. It is summarized in the following box.

The details will be omitted.

The normal/normal model

Suppose that μ is the mean of a normal distribution, and that the prior distribution for μ is normal with parameters a and b:

$$\mu \sim N(a, b).$$

Suppose that n observations, with mean $\overline{x}$, are made on X, where

$$X \sim N(\mu, \sigma^2)$$

and σ^2 is known.

Then the posterior distribution for μ, given the data, is normal:

$$\mu | \text{data} \sim N\left(\frac{\sigma^2 a + nb\overline{x}}{\sigma^2 + nb}, \frac{\sigma^2 b}{\sigma^2 + nb} \right). \tag{8.5}$$

Example 8.4   Normal/normal model for Alzheimer's progression

In Activity 5.10, the natural progression of Alzheimer's disease was considered. The parameter of interest is θ, the mean change in the value of an index measuring various aspects of short-term memory, one year after the diagnosis of Alzheimer's disease. Negative values indicate deterioration, positive values indicate improvement. The changes in the index values may be assumed to be normally distributed, $N(\theta, 100)$.

A study is undertaken by a researcher whose prior for θ is $N(-25, 64)$. The progression of disease in 20 newly-diagnosed patients with Alzheimer's is monitored, and for these 20 patients, the sample mean of the change in index values is -36. Using Formula (8.5), the researcher's posterior is normal with mean and variance given by

$$\text{mean} = \frac{\sigma^2 a + nb\overline{x}}{\sigma^2 + nb} = \frac{100 \times (-25) + 20 \times 64 \times (-36)}{100 + 20 \times 64} \simeq -35.2,$$

$$\text{variance} = \frac{\sigma^2 b}{\sigma^2 + nb} = \frac{100 \times 64}{100 + 20 \times 64} \simeq 4.64.$$

Note that the posterior mean, -35.2, is closer to the sample mean of the observations, -36, than to the prior mean, -25. This indicates that the data contribute more than the prior to the posterior distribution. Also notice that the posterior variance is much smaller than the prior variance, indicating that there is less uncertainty about the value of θ after observing the data.   ♦

Activity 8.4   Posterior for memory test improvement

In Example 5.2, a normal prior was suggested for θ, the mean improvement on a memory test of patients suffering from temporal lobe epilepsy who do not have surgery. In Activity 6.9, assessed values of the mode and quartiles of the prior for θ gave the prior distribution $N(10, 55)$.

The test scores for two tests for each of twelve patients are given in Table 8.3.

Table 8.3   Test scores and improvement for twelve patients

Patient	1	2	3	4	5	6	7	8	9	10	11	12
First test	71	75	98	107	86	89	101	69	76	103	88	117
Second test	69	84	110	99	109	99	96	85	86	111	103	119
Improvement	−2	9	12	−8	23	10	−5	16	10	8	15	2

Let X be the improvement in score from the first test to the second test for a randomly chosen patient. Assume that X is normally distributed with mean θ. In the general population, the improvement in scores for these tests was shown to have variance 90. Therefore it is reasonable to assume that the variance of the improvement for epilepsy patients is known and is also equal to 90. Thus $X \sim N(\theta, 90)$.

The observed values of X for the twelve patients are given in Table 8.3. Use these data to find the posterior distribution for θ.

8.4   Using uniform priors

Although uniform priors are not conjugate priors, their use is widespread with binomial, Poisson and normal data. Moreover, when combined with binomial, Poisson or normal data, suitably chosen uniform priors produce beta, gamma and normal posteriors, respectively. So the posteriors produced when using these uniform priors are the same as the distributions produced with conjugate analyses (although the posterior parameters are different). An illustration for binomial data is given in Example 8.5.

Example 8.5   Uniform prior for trust in politicians

In Example 8.1, a beta prior $\text{Beta}(a, b)$ was used for θ, the proportion of individuals who trust politicians to tell the truth. The likelihood for θ, given the information that 11 out of 50 adults interviewed said they did trust politicians to tell the truth, is given by

$$L(\theta) = \binom{50}{11} \theta^{11} (1 - \theta)^{39}.$$

If the prior for θ is uniform $U(0, 1)$, then

$$f(\theta) = 1, \quad 0 \le \theta \le 1.$$

Hence, using (8.1), the posterior for θ is given by

$$f(\theta | X = 11) = k \times \binom{50}{11} \theta^{11} (1 - \theta)^{39} \times 1$$

$$= k^* \times \theta^{11} (1 - \theta)^{39},$$

where k^* is a constant (not involving θ) which ensures that the area under the posterior density is 1. So the posterior density has the form of a beta density with parameters $a = 12$ and $b = 40$. ◆

The beta density is given in Formula (5.2).

Activity 8.5 *Uniform prior with binomial data*

Suppose that data $X = x$ are collected, and that X can be modelled by a binomial distribution $B(n, \theta)$, where θ is in the interval $[0, 1]$. A uniform prior $U(0, 1)$ is used for θ. Use the fact that the Beta$(1, 1)$ distribution is the same as $U(0, 1)$ to show that the posterior for θ is Beta$(1 + x, 1 + n - x)$.

Similar arguments can be used to obtain the posterior distribution for a Poisson mean or a normal mean, when the prior distribution is uniform. The main difference is that, in these cases, improper uniform priors must be used, because the range of a Poisson mean is $(0, \infty)$ and that of a normal mean is $(-\infty, \infty)$. The details are omitted. The posterior distributions obtained when using appropriate uniform priors are summarized in the following box.

Improper uniform priors were discussed briefly in Subsection 5.2.

The uniform/binomial, uniform/Poisson and uniform/normal models

If θ is a proportion with uniform prior $U(0, 1)$, then the posterior for θ, given an observation x on $X \sim B(n, \theta)$, is a beta distribution:

$$\theta|\text{data} \sim \text{Beta}(1 + x, 1 + n - x). \tag{8.6}$$

If μ is a Poisson mean with improper uniform prior on $[0, +\infty)$, then the posterior for μ, given n observations on $X \sim \text{Poisson}(\mu)$ with sample mean $\bar{x}$, is a gamma distribution:

$$\mu|\text{data} \sim \text{Gamma}(n\bar{x}, n). \tag{8.7}$$

If μ is a normal mean with improper uniform prior on $(-\infty, \infty)$, then the posterior for μ, given n observations with sample mean $\bar{x}$ on $X \sim N(\mu, \sigma^2)$, where σ^2 is known, is a normal distribution:

$$\mu|\text{data} \sim N\left(\bar{x}, \frac{\sigma^2}{n}\right). \tag{8.8}$$

Example 8.6 *Uniform prior for botulism intoxication*

In Example 8.3, a gamma/Poisson conjugate analysis was carried out for μ, the mean number of cases of botulism intoxication per year in England and Wales. In this analysis, a gamma prior for μ was used, and combined with data for eight years ($n = 8$). The sample mean number of cases for these 8 years was $\bar{x} = 0.75$.

Now suppose that, instead of the gamma prior, an improper uniform prior is used. This prior represents ignorance about the value of μ, so that all values are considered equally likely. Using Formula (8.7), the posterior distribution for μ is gamma with parameters $a = n\bar{x} = 6$ and $b = n = 8$. Hence the posterior distribution for μ, given the data, is $\mu|\text{data} \sim \text{Gamma}(6, 8)$. ◆

Activity 8.6 *Uniform prior for progression of Alzheimer's*

A normal/normal conjugate analysis to obtain the posterior distribution for μ, the mean change in a short-term memory index in the year following a diagnosis of Alzheimer's disease, was described in Example 8.4. The variance σ^2 is known to be 100. Data on 20 patients were collected, and the sample mean change in the index value was -36.

(a) Obtain the posterior distribution for μ, given these data, using an improper uniform prior for μ.

(b) In Example 8.4, the posterior distribution obtained with a normal prior was
$N(-35.2, 4.64)$. Compare this posterior with the one you obtained in
part (a). How do you explain the similarity or otherwise of the two posterior
distributions?

There are two main advantages to using conjugate analyses, or analyses with
uniform priors. The first is that they are quick and easy to use mathematically, so
a computer is not needed for calculating posteriors (although a computer is
certainly useful for drawing the prior, posterior and likelihood). The second
advantage is that it is easy to see how the data have influenced your beliefs. Since
the prior and posterior are members of the same family of distributions, they can
be compared very easily.

However, it is worth pointing out at this stage that a conjugate analysis may not
always be possible, or in fact desirable. Undertaking non-conjugate Bayesian
analyses is discussed in Parts III and IV of this book.

8.5   Exploring conjugate analyses and uniform priors

In this subsection, you will use *LearnBayes* to investigate binomial, Poisson and
normal likelihoods to see how they are affected by the data. You will also carry
out the full prior to posterior conjugate analyses you studied earlier in this section,
and explore how the posterior is affected by changing the prior or the data.

*Refer to Chapters 4 and 5 of Computer Book 4 for the work in this
subsection.*

Summary of Section 8

In this section, conjugate analyses have been discussed: the beta/binomial,
gamma/Poisson and normal/normal models have been described. Analyses using
uniform priors have also been discussed briefly. Plots of the prior, the likelihood
and the posterior have been used to assess the relative contributions of the prior
and the data to the posterior. You have used *LearnBayes* to explore normal,
binomial and Poisson likelihoods and to undertake conjugate analyses.

Exercises on Section 8

Exercise 8.1   Paediatric cardiology: other priors

Data on heart failure in babies were described in Activity 8.2. In a sample of
58 babies with transposition of the arteries, 5 had heart failure. In that activity,
you obtained the posterior for θ, the probability that a baby with transposition of
the arteries has heart failure, when the prior is Beta$(1.42, 5.13)$.

(a) Obtain the posterior distribution when the prior is Beta$(2, 6)$.

(b) Obtain the posterior distribution when the prior is Beta$(20, 60)$.

(c) Discuss the relative contributions of the prior and the data to the posterior
for each of the analyses in parts (a) and (b).

Exercise 8.2   Failure of coolant system in nuclear reactors

In Activity 8.3, you obtained the posterior distribution for θ, the failure rate of
the high pressure coolant injection system, when the prior is Gamma$(4.7, 4.8)$.
For the data in Table 8.2, $n = 4$ and $\bar{x} = 7/4$.

(a) Obtain the posterior distribution when the prior is Gamma$(4, 6)$.

(b) Obtain the posterior distribution using an improper uniform prior.

9 Bayesian inference

The final stage of a Bayesian prior to posterior analysis is to make inferences about the unknown parameter θ. With the Bayesian approach, all current information regarding θ is contained in the posterior distribution. Simply stating the distribution of the posterior — for example, Beta$(16, 64)$ — may not be very helpful, as it may be difficult to visualize it. A plot of the posterior is always useful as it gives a picture of the posterior density and its overall shape. The posterior should also be summarized using numerical summaries.

In Subsection 9.1, summaries for the location and spread are discussed. Methods for summarizing posterior uncertainty in θ are described in Subsection 9.2. In Subsection 9.3, you will use *LearnBayes* to obtain these summaries.

9.1 Summarizing the posterior

The measures of location that are commonly used with the posterior are the same as those used for summarizing the distribution of sample data — namely the mean, the median and the mode. The mean, the median and the mode coincide if the distribution has a single mode and is symmetric. However, for skew distributions, the median and the mode are usually more informative than the mean. In this subsection, the posterior mode, which is the most likely value for θ after observing the data, will generally be used to summarize the location of the posterior. The mode will be used because it is easily calculated by hand for all three of the conjugate posteriors that have been discussed. Also, the mode has often been used when specifying priors, so it is useful to compare the posterior and prior modes.

In Parts III and IV, the median and the mean will often be used to summarize the location rather than the mode, as they are easy to calculate using a computer.

Example 9.1 Posterior mode for nuclear reactor failure rate

In Activity 8.3, a Gamma$(4.7, 4.8)$ prior was used for θ, the failure rate of the HPCI system. The mode of a Gamma(a, b) distribution is given by Formula (5.5):

$$\text{mode} = \frac{a - 1}{b}.$$

Thus

$$\text{prior mode} = \frac{4.7 - 1}{4.8} \simeq 0.77.$$

You found that the posterior distribution is Gamma$(11.7, 8.8)$. Thus

$$\text{posterior mode} = \frac{11.7 - 1}{8.8} \simeq 1.22.$$

A plot of the posterior was given in Figure 8.2.

Thus the information from the data has increased the mode. The data suggest that the most likely value for θ is higher than the experts thought. In particular, the most likely value for the failure rate of the HPCI system is now believed to be greater than 1. ◆

Activity 9.1 Posterior mode for memory test improvement

In Activity 6.9, you found that a prior for θ, the mean improvement on the memory test of epilepsy patients who do not have surgery, is $N(10, 55)$. In Activity 8.4, you calculated the posterior for θ to be $N(7.8, 6.6)$. A plot of the prior, likelihood and posterior is given in Figure 9.1.

Summarize the location of the prior and the posterior for θ, and describe how the information from the data has altered the location.

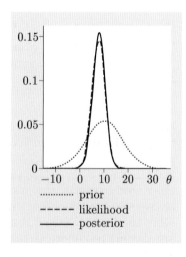

Figure 9.1 Prior, likelihood and posterior for mean improvement on memory tests

Activity 9.2   *Posterior mode for trust in politicians*

In Activity 8.1, you found four beta posteriors for θ, the proportion of individuals who trust politicians to tell the truth. The four beta priors considered were Beta(5, 7), Beta(60, 90), Beta(5, 2) and Beta(110, 28). Priors Beta(5, 7) and Beta(60, 90) both have mode 0.4, and priors Beta(5, 2) and Beta(110, 28) both have mode 0.8. You found that after observing $X = 11$ from a $B(50, \theta)$ distribution, the posteriors for these priors are Beta(16, 46), Beta(71, 129), Beta(16, 41) and Beta(121, 67), respectively. Plots of these posteriors, together with their corresponding priors and likelihoods, are shown in Figure 9.2.

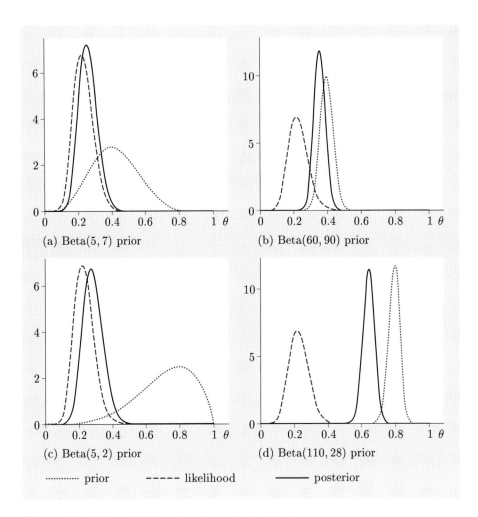

Figure 9.2   Prior, likelihood and posterior for θ

(a) Calculate the mode for each posterior.

(b) Within each pair of priors with the same mode, for which prior was the location affected more by the data? Explain why this is so.

The spread of the posterior represents the posterior uncertainty about θ: the larger the posterior spread, the larger is the posterior uncertainty. The spread of the posterior distribution is commonly summarized in the same way as the spread of the distribution of sample data is summarized — namely, using the variance and standard deviation. Alternatively, quantiles can be used, and compared to those used to specify the prior distribution. The variance and standard deviation are calculated easily for normal, beta and gamma posterior distributions. On the other hand, calculating quantiles is trickier and, particularly in the case of beta and gamma posteriors, is best left to a computer. Therefore only the variance and standard deviation will be used in this book for summarizing the spread of the posterior distribution. In Subsection 9.3, you will use *LearnBayes* to calculate posterior quantiles.

Example 9.2   Posterior variance for nuclear reactor failure rate

In Activity 8.3, the posterior for θ, the failure rate of the HPCI system, was calculated to be Gamma$(11.7, 8.8)$. The variance of a Gamma(a, b) distribution is a/b^2, so the posterior variance for θ is given by

$$\text{posterior variance} = \frac{11.7}{8.8^2} \simeq 0.15.$$

The variance for the prior, Gamma$(4.7, 4.8)$, is given by

$$\text{prior variance} = \frac{4.7}{4.8^2} \simeq 0.2.$$

The posterior variance is smaller than the prior variance, indicating that there is less uncertainty about θ after observing the data than there was before.   ◆

Activity 9.3   Posterior variance for memory test improvement

In Activity 6.9, you found that a prior for θ, the mean improvement on the memory test of an epilepsy patient who does not have surgery, is $N(10, 55)$. In Activity 8.4, you calculated the posterior for θ to be $N(7.8, 6.6)$. Summarize the posterior uncertainty about θ, and comment on how the data have affected the uncertainty about θ.

Notice that in both Example 9.2 and Activity 9.3, the posterior variance was smaller than the prior variance. Since the posterior brings together the two sources of information about θ — the prior and the data — the posterior variance is generally smaller than the prior variance. Thus you might expect to be less uncertain about θ after observing data than before. However, there are instances when the posterior variance is larger than the prior variance. This is illustrated in Example 9.3.

Example 9.3   Posterior variance for trust in politicians

Suppose that Beta$(150, 38)$ is used as a prior for θ, the proportion of individuals who trust politicians to tell the truth. This is quite a strong prior, with mode 0.8 and standard deviation 0.029. The prior is shown in Figure 9.3.

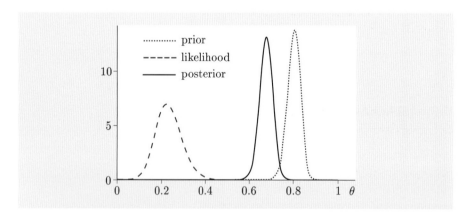

Figure 9.3   Beta$(150, 38)$ prior, likelihood and posterior

Out of a sample of 50 people interviewed, 11 said they trusted politicians to tell the truth. Thus the observed proportion is 0.22, which is very much smaller than the prior mode of 0.8. The data are said to **conflict** with the prior beliefs. This conflict is represented in Figure 9.3 by the lack of overlap between the prior and the likelihood.

Since a strong prior was chosen for θ, representing little uncertainty about θ, and the data conflict with the prior beliefs, the data might be expected to make you less sure about θ after observing the data than before. The posterior shown in Figure 9.3 lies between the prior and the likelihood, and certainly does not appear to be any less spread out than the prior. Indeed, the posterior standard deviation is 0.03, which is slightly larger than the prior standard deviation. ♦

As well as numerical summaries of the posterior, probabilities calculated from the posterior are also often of interest. This is illustrated in Example 9.4.

Example 9.4 Posterior probability for nuclear reactor failure rate

In Example 9.1, θ is the failure rate of the HPCI system. Suppose that θ_c represents some critical threshold value. Thus there is particular interest in the posterior probability that the failure rate of the HPCI system is greater than θ_c. For example, suppose that $\theta_c = 1$. The posterior probability that θ is greater than 1, given the data, may be obtained by calculating $P(\theta > 1|\text{data})$ from the posterior distribution Gamma$(11.7, 8.8)$. ♦

You will learn how to use *LearnBayes* to calculate this probability in Subsection 9.3.

Activity 9.4 Posterior probability for memory test improvement

In Activity 8.4, you found that the posterior for θ, the mean improvement on the memory test of an epilepsy patient who does not have surgery, is $N(7.8, 6.6)$. Calculate the posterior probability that there is an improvement on the memory test, that is, calculate the posterior probability that θ is greater than 0, given the data.

Recall that if $\theta \sim N(a, b)$, then
$$Z = \frac{\theta - a}{\sqrt{b}} \sim N(0, 1).$$

9.2 Credible intervals

Another way of summarizing the posterior distribution is to give an interval within which most of the distribution lies. Such an interval provides an interval estimate for θ, and is referred to as a **credible interval**. Credible intervals are defined in the following box.

Credible intervals

An interval (l, u) is a $100(1 - \alpha)\%$ **credible interval** for a parameter θ if the posterior probability that $l \leq \theta \leq u$, given the data, is equal to $1 - \alpha$:

$$P(l \leq \theta \leq u|\text{data}) = 1 - \alpha.$$

The probability $1 - \alpha$ is the **credibility level** of the interval.

Example 9.5   *Credible interval for memory test improvement*

In Activity 8.4, you found that the posterior for θ, the mean improvement on the memory test of epilepsy patients who do not have surgery, is $N(7.8, 6.6)$. Consider the interval $(l, u) = (2.76, 12.84)$. The credibility level of this interval is given by

$$P(2.76 \leq \theta \leq 12.84) = P\left(\frac{2.76 - 7.8}{\sqrt{6.6}} \leq Z \leq \frac{12.84 - 7.8}{\sqrt{6.6}}\right)$$

$$\simeq P(-1.96 \leq Z \leq 1.96)$$

$$= P(Z \leq 1.96) - P(Z < -1.96)$$

$$= 0.95.$$

Recall that if $\theta \sim N(a, b)$, then

$$Z = \frac{\theta - a}{\sqrt{b}} \sim N(0, 1).$$

Hence $(2.76, 12.84)$ is a 95% credible interval for θ.   ◆

Example 9.6   *Another credible interval for memory test improvement*

If θ is defined as in Example 9.5, then

$$P(3.3 \leq \theta \leq 13.8) = P\left(\frac{3.3 - 7.8}{\sqrt{6.6}} \leq Z \leq \frac{13.8 - 7.8}{\sqrt{6.6}}\right)$$

$$\simeq P(-1.75 \leq Z \leq 2.34)$$

$$\simeq 0.95.$$

Hence $(3.3, 13.8)$ is also a 95% credible interval for θ.   ◆

As illustrated in Examples 9.5 and 9.6, for any specified credibility level $1 - \alpha$, there can be more than one $100(1 - \alpha)\%$ credible interval for θ. In fact, there are usually many $100(1 - \alpha)\%$ credible intervals for θ. Therefore a further criterion is required in order to choose between the possible intervals. One criterion for posteriors with a single mode is to choose the $100(1 - \alpha)\%$ credible interval that contains the most likely values of θ. In this case, if θ_1 is any value of θ within the interval, and θ_2 is any value of θ outside the interval, then the posterior density at θ_1 must be no less than the posterior density at θ_2. Such an interval is referred to as a **highest posterior density** (HPD) interval.

In Figure 9.4, whenever θ_1 is within the interval (l, u) and θ_2 is outside the interval, $f(\theta_1|\text{data}) \geq f(\theta_2|\text{data})$, so the interval (l, u) is an HPD interval.

If the posterior has more than one mode, then there may not be a single HPD interval. However, you will not meet any such posteriors in this book.

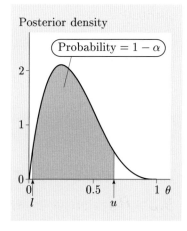

Figure 9.4   An HPD $100(1 - \alpha)\%$ credible interval for θ

Calculating the end-points of an HPD interval is often difficult, so it is more common to calculate **equal-tailed** credible intervals than HPD credible intervals. For an equal-tailed credible interval, the probability that the parameter's value is below the lower end of the credible interval is equal to the probability that it is above the upper end of the interval. For any $100(1 - \alpha)\%$ credible interval (l, u) for θ,

$$P(l \leq \theta \leq u|\text{data}) = 1 - \alpha.$$

Hence, if a $100(1 - \alpha)\%$ credible interval (l, u) is equal-tailed, then

$$P(\theta < l|\text{data}) = P(\theta > u|\text{data}) = \tfrac{1}{2}\alpha.$$

Thus l is the $\alpha/2$-quantile and u is the $(1 - \alpha/2)$-quantile of the posterior distribution.

When the distribution of θ is symmetric and unimodal, equal-tailed intervals are the same as HPD intervals. However, when the posterior distribution is skew, an equal-tailed interval will be slightly longer than the HPD interval with the same credibility level. This is illustrated in Example 9.7.

Example 9.7 HPD and equal-tailed credible intervals for trust in politicians

Let θ denote the proportion of individuals who trust politicians to tell the truth. In Activity 8.1, you found that the posterior distribution for the prior Beta$(5,7)$ is Beta$(16,46)$. The 95% HPD interval for this beta posterior is $(0.153, 0.367)$, so the length of the HPD interval is $0.367 - 0.153 = 0.214$. To obtain the corresponding equal-tailed interval, the 0.025-quantile and the 0.975-quantile of Beta$(16,46)$ are required. These quantiles are 0.158 and 0.373, so the 95% equal-tailed interval for θ is $(0.158, 0.373)$. Its length is 0.215, just a little longer than the HPD interval. ◆

The HPD interval and the beta quantiles were calculated using *LearnBayes*.

Activity 9.5 HPD and equal-tailed credible intervals for memory test improvement

In Example 9.5, you saw that the interval $(2.76, 12.84)$ is a 95% credible interval for θ, the mean improvement on a memory test of epilepsy patients who do not have surgery. The posterior for θ is $N(7.8, 6.6)$.

(a) Show that the interval $(2.76, 12.84)$ is both an equal-tailed credible interval and an HPD credible interval.

(b) Calculate the 99% equal-tailed credible interval for the parameter θ.

It is important to note that a Bayesian credible interval is *not* a classical confidence interval. In classical statistics, a parameter is not allowed to have a distribution. Thus, in classical statistics, the parameter θ is either inside a confidence interval or outside it. Thus, for example, $P(0.2 \leq \theta \leq 4.7)$ is 1 if θ lies between 0.2 and 4.7, and 0 if it does not. However, in Bayesian statistics, the parameter θ has a posterior distribution representing beliefs about θ, and hence $P(0.2 \leq \theta \leq 4.7)$ can take any value between 0 and 1, depending on the posterior.

Despite their conceptual differences, classical $100(1-\alpha)\%$ confidence intervals often have similar or identical end-points to the corresponding Bayesian $100(1-\alpha)\%$ credible intervals when the Bayesian prior distribution is noninformative.

9.3 Bayesian inference in practice

In this subsection, you will use *LearnBayes* for Bayesian inference in conjugate analyses. Using the software, you will calculate numerical summaries of the posterior, as well as HPD and equal-tailed credible intervals.

Refer to Chapter 6 of Computer Book 4 for the work in this subsection.

Summary of Section 9

In this section, methods of Bayesian inference have been presented. Obtaining a plot of the posterior is always helpful. The mode has been used to summarize the posterior location, and the variance or standard deviation to summarize the spread of the posterior in conjugate analyses. You have compared posterior and prior summaries, and obtained posterior probabilities. Credible intervals have been defined, and you have learned how to obtain HPD and equal-tailed credible intervals. You have used *LearnBayes* to obtain numerical summaries, including posterior quantiles and probabilities, and to calculate credible intervals.

Exercises on Section 9

Exercise 9.1   Posterior variances for trust in politicians

In Activity 8.1, you found four beta posteriors for θ, the proportion of individuals who trust politicians to tell the truth. The priors considered were Beta(5, 7), Beta(60, 90), Beta(5, 2) and Beta(110, 28). Priors Beta(5, 7) and Beta(60, 90) both have mode 0.4, and priors Beta(5, 2) and Beta(110, 28) both have mode 0.8. After observing $X = 11$ from $B(50, \theta)$, the posteriors for these priors were Beta(16, 46), Beta(71, 129), Beta(16, 41) and Beta(121, 67), respectively. The prior standard deviations for the four priors are given in Table 9.1, together with their respective beta posteriors and posterior standard deviations.

Table 9.1   Prior and posterior distributions, with standard deviations

Prior	Standard deviation	Posterior	Standard deviation
Beta(5, 7)	0.137	Beta(16, 46)	0.055
Beta(60, 90)	0.040	Beta(71, 129)	0.034
Beta(5, 2)	0.160	Beta(16, 41)	0.059
Beta(110, 28)	0.034	Beta(121, 67)	0.035

Notice that for priors Beta(5, 7) and Beta(5, 2), the difference between the prior standard deviation and the posterior standard deviation is far greater than for the prior Beta(60, 90). In addition, for prior Beta(110, 28), the prior standard deviation is less than the posterior standard deviation (to three decimal places). Explain these results.

Exercise 9.2   Diameters of tree trunks

The diameter of a tree trunk is an important variable in forestry. Suppose that the posterior distribution of the average diameter (in mm) of a tree trunk in a particular forest is $N(35, 38.1)$. Determine a 95% equal-tailed credible interval for the average diameter of tree trunks in the forest. Would the 95% HPD interval be shorter than this? Explain your answer.

Exercise 9.3   HPD and equal-tailed credible intervals

Figure 9.5 shows the posterior distribution for a parameter θ.

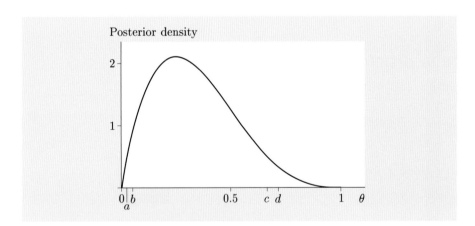

Figure 9.5   Posterior distribution for θ

Four values of θ are marked on Figure 9.5: a, b, c and d.

(a) One pair of values from a, b, c and d are the end-points of an HPD credible interval. Identify this interval.

(b) One pair of values from a, b, c and d are the end-points of an equal-tailed credible interval. Identify this interval (with the same credibility level as the HPD interval that you identified in part (a)).

Part III Bayesian inference via simulation

Introduction to Part III

In Parts I and II, you saw that it is not too difficult to implement a Bayesian analysis for an unknown quantity θ provided that beliefs about its value, before observing any data, are expressed through a conjugate prior distribution. However, a conjugate prior is not always appropriate for representing the prior beliefs. Furthermore, the posterior distribution for an unknown quantity cannot always be expressed in a neat mathematical form, such as that of a standard probability distribution.

In Section 10, two examples are described in which the mathematical calculations necessary to obtain the posterior distribution are either impossible or are beyond the scope of this course. Stochastic simulation, which is introduced in Section 11, is a simple, yet powerful, general technique that allows progress to be made in such situations. Some of the advantages offered by this simulation-based approach to inference are described. In Section 12, the software package WinBUGS is introduced and used for sampling values from standard probability distributions. Analyses involving a function of one or more parameters are discussed in Section 13. Some of the problems encountered when the Bayesian model involves more than one unknown parameter, and how simulation can be used to address these problems, are discussed in Section 14. In Section 15, you will use WinBUGS to analyse the problems discussed in Sections 13 and 14.

10 Beyond a conjugate Bayesian analysis

Conjugate Bayesian analyses, as described in Section 8, have two important attributes. First and foremost, the updating of beliefs from prior to posterior is easy to perform mathematically. Secondly, a conjugate prior can be used to reflect a wide range of prior beliefs about an unknown quantity θ. But what happens if your prior beliefs cannot be represented adequately by any member of the appropriate conjugate family? And what can be done if there is no appropriate conjugate family of distributions?

Two situations, one in which a conjugate analysis does not seem appropriate, and one in which a conjugate analysis is too mathematically complicated to handle easily, are described in this section.

Example 10.1   Traffic intensity in Western Canada

Data were collected on the incidence of traffic bunching on a section of the Trans-Canada Highway (TCH), in Western Canada. The section of road, Ottertail Hill, is a 100% no-overtaking zone, and therefore is prone to traffic bunching together in what are called 'platoons'. An interval of less than 5 seconds between successive vehicles is necessary for them to be considered part of the same platoon. A single vehicle travelling freely is regarded as a platoon of size 1. The sizes of 402 platoons were recorded over a particular time period. The data are summarized in Table 10.1.

Archilla, R. and Morrall, J. (1996) Traffic characteristics on two-lane highway downgrades. *Transportation Research Part A: Policy and Practice*, **30**, 119–133.

Table 10.1   Platoon size on Ottertail Hill

Platoon size	1	2	3	4	5	6	7	8	9	≥ 10
Frequency	256	72	33	21	10	4	4	0	2	0

A model which is commonly used for data on vehicle clustering is the **Borel distribution**. If $X \sim \text{Borel}(\theta)$, where $0 < \theta < 1$, then the probability mass function of X is given by

$$p(x|\theta) = P(X = x|\theta) = \frac{e^{-\theta x}(\theta x)^{x-1}}{x!}, \quad x = 1, 2, 3, \dots .$$

In the context of vehicle clustering, the parameter θ is sometimes called the traffic intensity.   ◆

Activity 10.1   A prior distribution for the Borel parameter

An expert in traffic clustering wishes to make inferences about the traffic intensity parameter θ of the Borel distribution based on the data in Table 10.1. From past experience, and before observing the data from the TCH, he believes that the most likely value of θ is around 0.2, and that the probability that θ lies in the interval $(0.1, 0.6)$ is around 0.9.

Suggest a prior distribution for the parameter θ which reflects the expert's beliefs. You need not suggest parameter values for the distribution, but feel free to do so if you wish.

Example 10.2   Traffic intensity in Western Canada, continued

As discussed in Activity 10.1, a Beta(a, b) distribution, with a and b chosen to reflect the expert's beliefs, seems a natural choice of prior for θ. The Beta$(2.9, 8.6)$ density is shown in Figure 10.1.

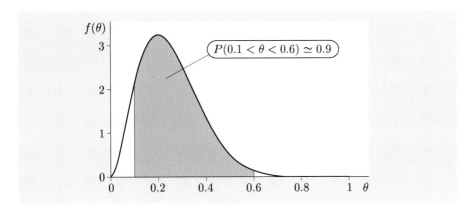

Figure 10.1   The Beta$(2.9, 8.6)$ density

As you can see, this density represents the expert's beliefs quite well.

Is the beta distribution conjugate to the Borel likelihood?

If a Borel distribution with parameter θ is used to model the data, then it can be shown that the likelihood of θ, given a sample of n observations with mean $\overline{x}$, has the form

$$L(\theta) = \text{constant} \times e^{-\theta n \overline{x}} \theta^{n(\overline{x}-1)}. \tag{10.1}$$

You do not need to know how to derive this likelihood.

The Beta(a, b) prior for θ has p.d.f.

$$f(\theta) = \text{constant} \times \theta^{a-1}(1 - \theta)^{b-1}.$$

The beta density is given in Formula (5.2).

The posterior density is obtained using Formula (8.1):

$$\text{posterior} = k \times \text{likelihood} \times \text{prior}.$$

Using this result, the posterior density can be shown to have the following form:

$$f(\theta|\text{data}) = K \times \theta^{a+n(\overline{x}-1)-1}(1 - \theta)^{b-1}e^{-\theta n \overline{x}}, \quad 0 < \theta < 1,$$

where K is a constant that ensures the area under $f(\theta|\text{data})$ is equal to 1.

Since this density does not have the form of a beta p.d.f., the beta prior is *not* conjugate to the Borel likelihood. Moreover, the posterior density is not that of a standard probability distribution, and the constant K is also very difficult to compute mathematically.

Therefore, if the beta prior is to be used for the Borel parameter θ (and it did seem sensible to do so), then in order to make inferences about θ, some other method is required.

Note that there are no other suitable candidates for a prior defined on $(0, 1)$ among the probability distributions discussed in Part II. And although there is a conjugate prior for the Borel likelihood, it is not a standard probability distribution, and it is difficult to work with. Therefore it will not be considered here. ◆

Another situation in which finding the posterior distribution is not straightforward is described in Example 10.3. In this case, a function of two unknown model parameters is of interest, rather than the parameters themselves.

Example 10.3   Can dogs detect bladder cancer?

A study was undertaken to investigate whether dogs, with their exceptional sense of smell, can detect bladder cancer from the smell of a person's urine.

Six dogs of different breeds, ages and sexes were trained to detect a urine sample from an individual with bladder cancer that was placed among six control specimens from individuals who did not have bladder cancer. In the testing phase of the experiment, each dog was faced with seven urine samples and was required to lie down next to the one it thought had traces of bladder cancer. This process was performed nine times, using different samples, for each dog.

Primary interest in this study concerned whether the dogs could detect the urine samples with bladder cancer better than would be expected 'by chance alone'.

Willis, C.M. *et al.* (2004) Olfactory detection of human bladder cancer by dogs: proof of principle study. *British Medical Journal*, **329**, 712–714.

However, four of the dogs had been trained using fresh urine samples, whereas the other two dogs had been trained using dried urine. Therefore an additional question that can be addressed from the data in this study is whether there is any difference between dogs trained using fresh urine samples and dogs trained using dried urine samples in their ability to detect bladder cancer.

Let θ_1 denote the proportion of urine samples from individuals with bladder cancer that are detected by dogs trained using fresh urine, and let θ_2 denote the corresponding proportion for dogs trained using dried urine. Before observing the data from the study, prior distributions for θ_1 and θ_2 need to be specified.

Of course, everyone is entitled to their own personal (prior) beliefs about these quantities — for example, you may think that fresh urine will lead to better detection than dried urine, and hence $\theta_1 > \theta_2$ — but for illustrative purposes, assume independent conjugate Beta$(1,1)$ priors for θ_1 and θ_2, that is,

$$\theta_1 \sim \text{Beta}(1,1), \quad \theta_2 \sim \text{Beta}(1,1).$$

Since the Beta$(1,1)$ prior is the same as the uniform prior $U(0,1)$, these priors are noninformative. They are consistent with prior beliefs that θ_1 and θ_2 are equally likely to take any value in the allowable range. They also convey the belief that θ_1 is just as likely to be greater than θ_2 as it is to be less than θ_2.

Suppose that in n_1 experiments involving dogs trained using fresh urine, the urine sample with bladder cancer is detected on x_1 occasions, and that in n_2 experiments involving dogs trained using dried urine, the urine sample with bladder cancer is detected on x_2 occasions. Suppose further that it is reasonable to assume that x_1 and x_2 are realizations of independent random variables X_1 and X_2 with binomial distributions:

$$X_1 \sim B(n_1, \theta_1), \quad X_2 \sim B(n_2, \theta_2).$$

The results of the study showed that of the 36 experiments involving dogs trained using fresh urine, the urine sample with bladder cancer was detected 18 times. Of the 18 experiments involving dogs trained using dried urine, the urine sample with bladder cancer was detected 4 times. Therefore

$$n_1 = 36, \quad x_1 = 18, \quad n_2 = 18, \quad x_2 = 4.$$

Conjugate analysis for a proportion was discussed in Subsection 8.1. You saw that with a Beta(a,b) prior, given data $X = x$ from $B(n,\theta)$, the posterior distribution is Beta$(a+x, b+n-x)$. It follows that the independent posterior distributions for θ_1 and θ_2 are as follows:

$$\theta_1|\text{data} \sim \text{Beta}(19,19), \quad \theta_2|\text{data} \sim \text{Beta}(5,15).$$

These distributions are illustrated in Figure 10.2.

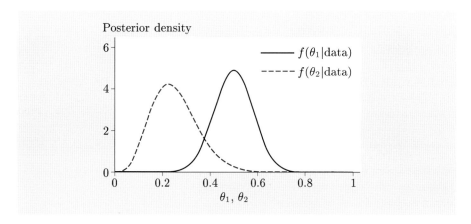

Figure 10.2   Posterior densities of θ_1 and θ_2

From Figure 10.2, it is clear that the likely values of θ_1 are generally higher than the likely values of θ_2. Also, for dogs trained using fresh urine, the proportion of samples from individuals with bladder cancer that are detected is likely to be greater than 0.4, whereas for dogs trained using dried urine, the proportion is likely to be less than 0.4. There is some overlap between the two posterior distributions in Figure 10.2, but is there a real difference between the two proportions?

The quantity of interest is d, the difference between the two proportions: $d = \theta_1 - \theta_2$. This is a function of the two parameters. In the Bayesian approach to statistics, inferences about the quantity d are based on its posterior distribution. Although d is a very simple function of θ_1 and θ_2, the required posterior density does not have a standard form. In fact, it takes the form of a **beta difference distribution**, which you will not find in many (if indeed any) statistical software packages. This far from universal availability, together with its complicated mathematical form, make using the beta difference distribution beyond the scope of this course.

Thus, even if conjugate priors are used for the two proportions, the distribution of the difference is not easy to work with. This is unsatisfactory since the difference between two binomial proportions is such a simple statistical concept.   ♦

Example 10.3 demonstrates that when interest lies in a function of unknown quantities, it may not be possible to obtain the posterior distribution in a standard form even though the posterior distributions for the original quantities are in a standard form. When interest lies in a simple function of a single unknown quantity, it may be possible to work out the form of the posterior distribution. However, this is unlikely to be possible for complicated functions or for functions of many unknown quantities. Clearly, a method for tackling such problems is needed. One such method, which can handle functions of unknown quantities, posterior distributions not based on conjugate prior beliefs and most other features of a realistic Bayesian analysis, is introduced in Section 11.

Summary of Section 10

In this section, two examples have been described that illustrate some of the situations where a Bayesian analysis cannot be performed in a straightforward way: for example, when a non-conjugate prior distribution is chosen; when a conjugate prior distribution does not exist; or when the posterior distribution for a function of one or more unknown quantities is required.

11 Stochastic simulation

In many areas of science and engineering, interest lies in the behaviour of a system that is too complex to study directly. When this is the case, one commonly used solution is to construct a model or experiment that mimics the real situation as closely as possible and to study that instead. For example, since the actual physical processes that contribute to the weather and climate are too complex to study directly, meteorologists use complex mathematical models for short-range weather forecasting and for longer-range climate prediction. This alternative to analysing the real system of interest is known as **simulation**.

A number of situations where a direct Bayesian analysis was not simple were described in Section 10. In this section, a method that has proved to be successful in a wide range of situations is introduced; this method is called **stochastic simulation**. Essentially, stochastic simulation involves obtaining samples of values from the probability distribution of the quantity of interest. When the posterior distribution of the quantity of interest in a Bayesian analysis cannot be obtained in the form of a standard probability distribution, one way forward is to *simulate* the posterior distribution through values sampled from the distribution. These samples can then be used for Bayesian inference.

The word *stochastic* simply means random.

There is nothing Bayesian about this general approach. It is simply an example of using a *sample* from a *population* to understand characteristics of the population. In the context of stochastic simulation, the population corresponds to the distribution of the parameter of interest, and the sample corresponds to the collection of values of the parameter that are obtained.

Stochastic simulation is often called **Monte Carlo** simulation, the Monte Carlo method, or, simply, Monte Carlo. The city of Monte Carlo in the Principality of Monaco is famous for its casino: the obvious association between gambling and random variation was thought to provide an attractive name for the subject! The use of the terminology 'Monte Carlo' as a synonym for stochastic simulation originated in the late 1940s and was popularized by mathematicians and physicists, who were beginning to use such methods for analysing complex problems in their own subjects. At the time, statisticians had been using simulation, or 'sampling methods', for several decades, albeit on a much smaller scale than that used by the physicists. To the statisticians, it was simply a rebranding of an already well-established method. Nevertheless, Monte Carlo has become a familiar and oft-used term in the modern statistical vocabulary.

In this section, attention is focused on how stochastic simulation can be used for making inferences. The details of how samples are obtained will not be considered here.

Stochastic simulation: the general idea

The basic idea behind stochastic simulation is as follows: to obtain information about an unknown parameter or quantity of interest, sample values from its distribution and study them. Suppose that interest lies in the posterior distribution for an unknown quantity θ. If a large number of values are sampled from this distribution, then they can be used to estimate features of the distribution, such as the overall shape, or the mean and variance.

The sampled values can be studied in a way analogous to the study of a random sample of data from a population: the values from a stochastic simulation are summarized by graphical and numerical methods, and used for making inferences about the distribution of the quantity of interest.

The true strength of simulation is that it can be used to analyse problems that are too complex to analyse mathematically — for example, when a non-conjugate Bayesian analysis is required. However, simulation methods are much more generally applicable and can be used for making inferences about distributions which have standard forms. Many of the ideas introduced in this section will be illustrated using values sampled from a standard distribution.

Graphical and numerical summaries

The first step in analysing simulated values is to display them graphically in order to obtain an idea of the overall shape of the underlying distribution — how skew it is, the most likely values, the range of plausible values, and so on. A graphical display which is appropriate when the quantity of interest is continuous is discussed in Example 11.1.

Example 11.1   Simulation of a beta posterior distribution

Data from an experiment to determine whether or not dogs can detect bladder cancer from the smell of a sample of urine were described in Example 10.3. Suppose that interest lies in θ_1, the proportion of samples identified correctly by dogs trained using fresh urine. In Example 10.3, you saw that if the Beta(1, 1) prior is used for θ_1, then given the observation that 18 out of 36 samples were identified correctly, the posterior distribution for θ_1 is Beta(19, 19), that is

$$\theta_1|\text{data} \sim \text{Beta}(19, 19).$$

Now imagine that you do not know what a Beta(19, 19) distribution looks like. To gain information about the distribution, $N = 100$ values are sampled independently from the distribution.

The sample size for a stochastic simulation is denoted N to distinguish it from the sample size of a set of data, which is denoted n.

A histogram of the simulated values from the posterior distribution for θ_1 is shown in Figure 11.1(a).

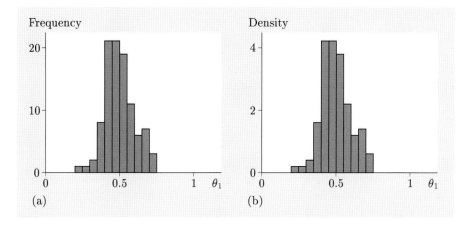

Figure 11.1   Simulated values from the Beta(19, 19) distribution:
(a) histogram (b) density histogram

In this histogram, the number of simulated values in a bin is represented by the height of the corresponding vertical bar. In Figure 11.1(b), the height of a bar represents the *density* or *relative frequency* of values in a bin. This histogram is a **density histogram**. A density histogram is obtained from an ordinary histogram by scaling the bars so that the total area of the bars is equal to one. The only difference between the two histograms is in the vertical scale used. Density histograms will be used from now on because they give a direct visual representation, and hence an estimate, of the true underlying probability density function. Also, they can be used to compare p.d.f.s when the samples involved are of different sizes.   ◆

Activity 11.1 Interpreting a histogram of simulated values

(a) What are the main features of the posterior distribution for θ_1 that can be inferred from the density histogram in Figure 11.1(b)?

(b) The Beta$(19, 19)$ density is shown in Figure 11.2. Explain whether or not the density histogram in Figure 11.1(b) provides a good estimate of the Beta$(19, 19)$ p.d.f.

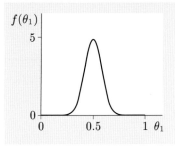

Figure 11.2 The Beta$(19, 19)$ density

The posterior distribution for an unknown parameter contains all the available information about the parameter. For a univariate posterior distribution, a plot of the p.d.f. encapsulates all this information. Even so, it is also useful to summarize the distribution by a few key quantities, such as the mode, the mean and the variance.

These quantities, and others, can be estimated by using the sampled values in the obvious way: simply estimate any quantity of interest by its equivalent value based on the sample. For example, if a parameter θ is of interest, and a sample of values of size N has been simulated from the posterior distribution for θ, then the posterior mean of θ can be estimated by the sample mean of the simulated values, and the standard deviation of the posterior for θ by the sample standard deviation.

This is exactly the same as the process of estimating features of a population based on a random sample of data from the population.

In Subsection 9.1, the mode was used to summarize the location of the posterior as it is easy to calculate by hand for simple conjugate models. However, when using simulation, it is easier to estimate the mean or the median of the posterior than it is to estimate the mode, so it is usual to summarize the location of the posterior using the mean or the median.

Activity 11.2 Estimating the median from a stochastic simulation

Given a sample of values from the posterior distribution for an unknown parameter θ, how would you estimate the posterior median of θ?

Example 11.2 Numerical summaries from simulated values

A sample of $N = 1000$ independent values was obtained from the Beta$(19, 19)$ posterior distribution for θ_1, the proportion of samples identified correctly by dogs trained using fresh urine. These sampled values were used to estimate various features of the posterior distribution, such as the mean, the median and the standard deviation. The sample estimates of these quantities (rounded to four decimal places) are given in Table 11.1, together with the true values for the Beta$(19, 19)$ distribution.

The sample size $N = 100$ was used in Example 11.1.

Table 11.1 Sample estimates and true values for Beta$(19, 19)$

Quantity	True value	Sample estimate
Mean	0.5	0.4995
Median	0.5	0.4995
Standard deviation	0.0801	0.0850

All the estimates are close to the true values they are estimating. The sample mean and the sample median are very close to the true values of the mean and median. Although the sample standard deviation differs rather more from the true value, it nevertheless gives a reasonable estimate. Of course, with a larger sample of simulated values, these estimates might be expected to be closer to the true values. The effect of sample size on the accuracy of estimates, and choice of sample size, will be discussed shortly. ◆

Estimating credible intervals

Another useful summary of the posterior for an unknown quantity θ is a **credible interval**. Recall that an interval is a $100(1 - \alpha)\%$ credible interval for θ if the probability that the true value of θ lies in the interval is $1 - \alpha$.

Suppose that you are interested in obtaining an equal-tailed $100(1 - \alpha)\%$ credible interval for the unknown quantity θ. The lower and upper limits of this credible interval can be estimated by simulating values from the distribution of θ and then calculating the sample $\alpha/2$-quantile and the sample $(1 - \alpha/2)$-quantile of the simulated values. These sample quantiles act as the lower and upper limits of the credible interval.

> Credible intervals were discussed in Subsection 9.2.

> HPD intervals are not easy to calculate using simulation, so they will not be considered further.

Example 11.3   An estimated credible interval

The $N = 1000$ values sampled independently from a Beta$(19, 19)$ distribution, that were summarized in Example 11.2, can also be used to estimate the equal-tailed 95% posterior credible interval for θ_1. For a 95% credible interval, the 0.025-quantile and the 0.975-quantile of the sampled values are required; these are 0.330 and 0.666. Therefore the estimated equal-tailed 95% posterior credible interval for θ_1 is $(0.330, 0.666)$. ◆

> θ_1 is the proportion of urine samples that are correctly identified by dogs trained using fresh urine.

Activity 11.3   Interpreting a credible interval

(a) What can you infer about the value of θ_1 from the estimated equal-tailed 95% credible interval of Example 11.3?

(b) The exact equal-tailed 95% credible interval, calculated directly using the Beta$(19, 19)$ distribution, is $(0.344, 0.656)$. Assess the accuracy of the estimate reported in Example 11.3. Suggest one way in which the accuracy of this estimate could be improved.

Sampling variability

Each time a sample is taken from a distribution, the values obtained are likely to be different. Consequently, with each different sample, different estimates of the various characteristics of the distribution will be obtained.

The random variation of samples from stochastic simulations is often called **sampling variability**. It is also referred to as **Monte Carlo variability** to indicate that the sample is based on a stochastic simulation rather than a sample of data from a population. Minimizing this sampling variability is an important aspect of stochastic simulation, as it is undesirable for inferences to vary greatly from sample to sample.

Suppose that interest lies in summarizing the posterior distribution for the quantity θ through its mean μ. Suppose also that the posterior distribution for θ has variance σ^2. The mean of a sample of N values from the posterior distribution is the natural estimate of the posterior mean μ. With each independent sample of size N from the posterior distribution, a different sample mean estimate will be obtained. The distribution of these sample means is the **sampling distribution** of the mean. The sampling distribution of the mean is a probability distribution with mean equal to μ, the posterior mean (and the quantity of interest), and variance σ^2/N.

This implies that, although the sample mean from a single sample is unlikely to be exactly equal to μ, it will give the right value on average, and hence it is a 'good' estimator of μ.

Furthermore, the variance of the sampling distribution depends on σ^2, the variance of the distribution of interest, and on the sample size N. When values are sampled independently, the variance of the sampling distribution decreases as

N increases, implying that the sample mean based on a large sample will be closer to the true value μ, on average, than the sample mean based on a smaller sample.

The standard deviation of the sampling distribution of the mean, which is equal to $\sigma/\sqrt{N}$, is frequently called the **standard error** of the mean. Essentially, it can be viewed as a measure of the *error* involved in using the sample mean to estimate the true (population) mean. When dealing with Monte Carlo simulations rather than samples of data, the standard error of the mean is often referred to as the **Monte Carlo standard error** of the mean, or the **MC error**, for short.

Here, *error* is used to mean the distance of the estimate from the true value.

The smaller the Monte Carlo standard error, the more accurate the estimates of the mean will be. As such, the Monte Carlo standard error provides a useful summary of the sampling variability from a simulation.

It is good statistical practice when reporting the sample mean to include its standard error in brackets following the estimate. This gives some indication of the accuracy of the estimate.

Example 11.4   Reporting simulation results

In Example 11.2, the sample mean was 0.4995. An estimate of the standard error of the mean based on the sample is 0.002 69. Therefore the sample mean, together with its standard error, would be reported as 0.4995 (0.002 69).   ◆

You will not be expected to calculate the MC error in this course. In practice, this is done using a computer.

In general, the larger the sample of simulated values, the more accurate inferences based on the sample will be. An important aspect of Monte Carlo simulation is that *you* have control over the sample size N. In theory, you can set N to be as large as you like. However, in practice, the physical limitations of the time taken to obtain the sample and the computer memory needed to store the sampled values place a constraint on the sample size. Therefore a compromise is needed between running a very large, time-consuming simulation which will produce highly accurate estimates and running a smaller, much quicker simulation.

One 'rule of thumb' that is sometimes used to determine the sample size N to be used in a stochastic simulation is that N should be chosen so that the estimate of the Monte Carlo standard error of the mean is less than about 5% of the sample standard deviation. This '5% rule of thumb' can be useful when more complicated simulation strategies are considered. However, in this course, the sample size $N = 10\,000$ will generally be advocated as a default large value.

Activity 11.4   The 5% rule of thumb

In Example 11.2, the sample mean of a sample of 1000 values simulated from the Beta$(19, 19)$ distribution was reported as 0.4995. The sample standard deviation was 0.0850, and the Monte Carlo standard error was 0.002 69. Use the 5% rule of thumb to decide whether the sample size used in the simulation was large enough.

Summary of Section 11

In this section, stochastic simulation has been introduced. You have seen how samples from the posterior distribution can be used to make inferences about an unknown quantity of interest. The density histogram has been introduced as an appropriate graphical display for simulated values from a continuous distribution. This provides a visual representation of the key features of a distribution. You have seen that any quantity of interest in the distribution being studied can be estimated by its equivalent value in the sample — for example, the mean of the distribution can be estimated by the sample mean, and a $100(1 - \alpha)\%$ credible interval can be estimated by calculating the sample $\alpha/2$-quantile and the sample

$(1 - \alpha/2)$-quantile of the simulated values. The effect of sample size on sampling variability has been discussed briefly, and the Monte Carlo standard error has been introduced as a measure of sampling variability for the mean estimate. You have seen that the Monte Carlo standard error depends on the sample size of the simulation, and that it can be reduced by taking a larger sample size.

Exercises on Section 11

Exercise 11.1   Estimating credible intervals using simulation

Simulation from the posterior distribution for a parameter θ is used to obtain an estimate of the equal-tailed 95% credible interval for θ. For a sample of $N = 1000$ values, the width of the estimated credible interval is 2.01. For a sample of $N = 10\,000$ values, the width of the estimated credible interval is 2.12.

(a) Explain briefly why the width of the estimated credible interval obtained using the sample of 10 000 values is not smaller than that of the interval obtained using the sample of 1000 values.

(b) Suppose that the analysis is to be repeated using the same prior for θ, but ten times as much data. The 95% credible interval for θ will be estimated by simulating a sample of $N = 10\,000$ values. Explain briefly whether you would expect the width of this estimated 95% credible interval to be greater than 2.12, less than 2.12, or similar to 2.12.

Exercise 11.2   Simulation sample size

The mean of the posterior distribution for a parameter θ is estimated from a sample of N values obtained by simulation. The sample mean is 3.8721, and the sample standard deviation is 0.2632. The Monte Carlo standard error is 0.0234.

Is the sample size N adequate? Explain your answer.

12   Stochastic simulation in practice

In Section 11, the basic ideas behind stochastic simulation for Bayesian inference were described.

In this section, the statistical software package WinBUGS is introduced. You will use this software to simulate from some simple probabilistic models, and to obtain graphical and numerical summaries for making inferences about quantities of interest.

Refer to Chapters 7, 8 and 9 of Computer Book 4 for the work in this section.

Summary of Section 12

In this section, some basic features of WinBUGS have been introduced. You have seen how a simple probabilistic model is defined in WinBUGS. You have also learned how to use WinBUGS to sample from models which are standard probability distributions, and then summarize the sampled values using graphical and numerical summaries.

13 Dealing with functions of unknown parameters

You may be wondering why anyone would want to use simulation in order to make inferences about a parameter with a standard probability distribution, as was the case in Section 11. Surely if you know the mathematical form of the distribution, then simulation tells you nothing more than you already know (and quite often tells you what you already know less accurately!). In this section, you will see that, even when dealing with a standard probability distribution, the mathematics involved can be complicated — for example, when the quantity of interest is a function of one or more unknown parameters. Fortunately, in such situations, a simulation-based approach to inference is straightforward.

Example 13.1 Estimating the sex ratio

Data are available on the numbers of (live) male births and female births in different UK health authorities. In Milton Keynes, in 2001, there were 1442 male births and 1388 female births. Suppose that you would like to use this information to make inferences about the underlying proportion of male (or female) births in the UK as a whole.

Office for National Statistics, 2001.

Let θ represent the proportion of male births (out of total births) in the UK. Suppose that a Beta$(5, 5)$ distribution is used to model prior uncertainty in the value of θ. This prior was chosen to reflect the uncontroversial belief that the proportion of male births is likely to be around 0.5 (that is, equal numbers of male and female births, on average). The prior density, which is shown in Figure 13.1, indicates a fairly weak prior belief in this assertion.

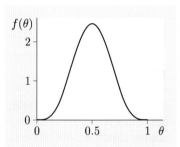

Figure 13.1 The Beta$(5, 5)$ density

Assuming that the proportion of male births in Milton Keynes is the same as that in the UK as a whole, the number of male births in Milton Keynes in 2001 can be modelled as an observation from the binomial distribution $B(n, \theta)$, where $n = 1442 + 1388 = 2830$, the total number of births in Milton Keynes in 2001. Using Result (8.3) for the beta/binomial model, combining the conjugate beta prior with the information from the data that there were $x = 1442$ male births, results in a Beta$(5 + 1442, 5 + 1388)$ posterior distribution for θ, that is,

$$\theta|\text{data} \sim \text{Beta}(1447, 1393).$$

Based on this posterior distribution, probability statements can be made about the likely values of θ. The exact posterior mean (obtained from the properties of the beta distribution) is 0.5095 (to four decimal places), and the equal-tailed 95% posterior credible interval is $(0.4911, 0.5279)$.

Traditionally, in studies of births of this type, the quantity of most interest is the ratio of male births to female births, $\phi = \theta/(1 - \theta)$, which is known as the sex ratio. A value of $\phi = 1$ indicates that the proportions of male and female births are equal.

In other contexts, this ratio is known as the odds.

To obtain the posterior distribution for ϕ would require some fairly complicated mathematics, as would deriving an expression for the posterior mean of ϕ. However, it is easy to simulate from the posterior distribution for θ as it is a standard probability distribution, namely a beta distribution. Applying the transformation $\theta/(1 - \theta)$ to each of the sampled values of θ gives a sample of values from the posterior distribution for the sex ratio ϕ. This sample of values can be used to make inferences about ϕ.

Thus, based on a sample of values from the posterior distribution for θ, inferences can be made about ϕ.

To illustrate the method, $N = 10\,000$ values for θ were sampled from its posterior distribution Beta$(1447, 1393)$. The first five values of this sample are in the second column of Table 13.1.

The values in the final column represent a sample from the posterior distribution for ϕ.

Table 13.1 Simulated values of θ and ϕ

i	θ_i	$1 - \theta_i$	$\phi_i = \dfrac{\theta_i}{1 - \theta_i}$
1	0.5111	0.4889	1.0454
2	0.4957	0.5043	0.9829
3	0.5098	0.4902	1.0400
4	0.5055	0.4945	1.0222
5	0.5076	0.4924	1.0309
⋮	⋮	⋮	⋮

Thus, with very little effort, a sample of $N = 10\,000$ values from the posterior distribution for ϕ can be obtained and used to make inferences about ϕ in the usual way. Figure 13.2 shows an estimate of the posterior p.d.f. for ϕ based on the sampled values.

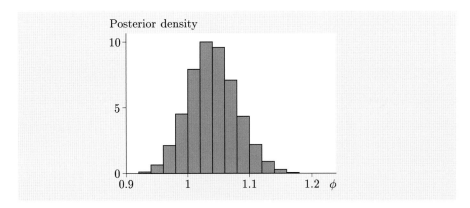

Figure 13.2   Density histogram of $N = 10\,000$ simulated values from the posterior distribution for the sex ratio $\phi = \theta/(1 - \theta)$

The distribution is unimodal and approximately symmetric about a central value of 1.04.

The sampled values from the posterior distribution for ϕ can be used to estimate the posterior mean, median and standard deviation. The estimates of these quantities are 1.040 (0.0004), 1.039 and 0.039, respectively. An estimate of the MC error is reported in brackets after the sample mean estimate. An estimate of the equal-tailed 95% credible interval for ϕ obtained from the simulated values is $(0.966, 1.121)$.   ◆

Activity 13.1   The posterior distribution for the sex ratio

It is generally accepted that there are more male births than female births in European populations, with the sex ratio usually considered to be 1.06. Does the information gained on the posterior distribution for ϕ from the sample of births in Milton Keynes support this view?

The ease with which posterior summaries were obtained in Example 13.1, without resorting to any complicated mathematics (only simple arithmetic!), illustrates one of the main advantages of a simulation-based approach to inference: simulation is often straightforward when the mathematics is not.

The general procedure for dealing with a function of an unknown parameter is summarized in the following box.

Inference for a function of an unknown parameter

Suppose that interest lies in making inferences about the parameter ϕ which is a function $g(\theta)$ of the parameter θ. If simulating values of θ is straightforward, then proceed as follows.

◇   Sample N values of θ, denoted $\theta_1, \theta_2, \ldots, \theta_N$.

◇   Apply the function g to each of the simulated values $\theta_1, \theta_2, \ldots, \theta_N$, to give values $\phi_1 = g(\theta_1)$, $\phi_2 = g(\theta_2)$, $\ldots$, $\phi_N = g(\theta_N)$. These values can be considered a simulation from the distribution of ϕ.

◇   Use these ϕ values to make inferences about ϕ.

In Example 13.1, you saw that it is straightforward to make inferences about a function of a parameter based on samples from the distribution of the parameter. In fact, it is just as easy to make inferences about a function of more than one parameter, as Example 13.2 illustrates.

Example 13.2   Difference between binomial proportions

An experiment in which dogs were tested to see whether or not they could detect bladder cancer from the smell of a sample of urine was described in Example 10.3. One question of interest was whether the ability to detect bladder cancer differed for dogs trained using fresh urine and dogs trained using dried urine.

The proportions of urine samples that are correctly identified by dogs trained on fresh urine and dried urine were denoted θ_1 and θ_2, respectively. With independent Beta$(1, 1)$ priors for θ_1 and θ_2, the independent posterior distributions for the two parameters were as follows:

$$\theta_1|\text{data} \sim \text{Beta}(19, 19), \quad \theta_2|\text{data} \sim \text{Beta}(5, 15).$$

The quantity of interest is the difference between the two proportions, $d = \theta_1 - \theta_2$. The posterior distribution for d takes the form of a beta difference distribution, whose use is beyond the scope of this course. Fortunately, inferences about d can be made based on simulation from its posterior distribution.

If a value of θ_1 is sampled from its posterior distribution, which is Beta$(19, 19)$, and, independently, a value of θ_2 is sampled from its posterior distribution, which is Beta$(5, 15)$, then a value from the posterior distribution for d is obtained by calculating the difference between the simulated values of θ_1 and θ_2.

A sample of $N = 10\,000$ pairs of values of θ_1 and θ_2 was obtained. For each pair of values, their difference $(\theta_1 - \theta_2)$ was calculated. These differences give a sample from the posterior distribution for d.

A density histogram of the $N = 10\,000$ simulated values from the posterior distribution for d is shown in Figure 13.3.

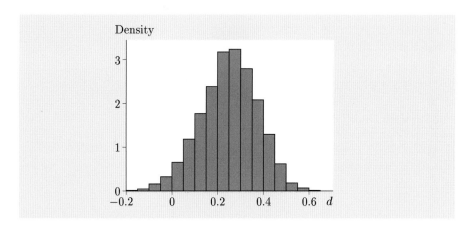

Figure 13.3   Density histogram of $N = 10\,000$ simulated values from the posterior distribution for d

Based on the simulated values, an estimate of the posterior mean of d, together with its MC error (in brackets), is 0.2496 (0.0012). An estimate of the equal-tailed 95% credible interval for d is $(-0.007, 0.477)$.   ◆

Activity 13.2 Interpreting simulation results

Using the simulation results which are summarized at the end of Example 13.2, describe the main features of the posterior distribution for d. In your description, comment on the shape of the p.d.f. Also give a range of plausible values for the true difference and a single value that you might use as an estimate of d.

Summary of Section 13

In this section, the ease with which transformations of parameters can be dealt with using a simulation-based approach to inference has been illustrated.

Exercise on Section 13

Exercise 13.1   IQ tests

IQ tests are usually designed so that the scores obtained are normally distributed with mean 100 and standard deviation 15.

The mean score on a new IQ test is known to be 100. A model for the score on this test is

$$X \sim N(100, \sigma^2).$$

This is a normal distribution with unknown standard deviation σ.

Following standard practice, a conjugate gamma prior distribution is adopted for the precision $\tau = 1/\sigma^2$, namely $\tau \sim \text{Gamma}(1 + 1/15^2, 1)$. The parameters of the gamma prior were chosen so that the mode of the prior is $1/225$, the theoretical precision of the IQ test (if it is working correctly). The new IQ test was given to a random sample of 40 people. The scores obtained and the prior were used to calculate the posterior distribution for τ using Result (8.4). For these 40 IQ scores, the posterior distribution is $\tau|\text{data} \sim \text{Gamma}(21.004\,44, 5220)$.

The precision was defined in Example 5.9.

The mode of $\text{Gamma}(a, b)$ is $(a - 1)/b$.

A sample of $N = 10\,000$ values was taken from the posterior distribution for τ.

(a) Interest lies in the posterior distribution for σ, the standard deviation of the scores. Describe how the simulated values for τ could be used to make inferences about σ.

(b) The first five values of τ were 0.0057, 0.0050, 0.0048, 0.0039, 0.0027. Calculate the first five simulated values from the posterior distribution for σ.

14 Bayesian inference for two parameters

A Bayesian analysis is more complicated when the Bayesian model involves more than one unknown parameter. Some of the complexities encountered when dealing with multi-parameter problems are outlined in this section.

In Subsection 14.1, a particular Bayesian model with two unknown parameters is introduced — the normal model with unknown mean and variance — and a conjugate Bayesian analysis for the parameters of this model is described. Quite often, the distributions of the unknown parameters considered separately — that is, their *marginal distributions* — are of most interest. Determining marginal distributions from joint distributions is discussed in Subsection 14.2. The analysis of samples simulated from joint and marginal posterior distributions is discussed in Subsection 14.3.

14.1 Normal model with unknown mean and variance

In 1798, the English scientist Henry Cavendish (1731–1810) made several experimental measurements of the density of the Earth (in g/cm^3). Interest lies in using Cavendish's measurements, and any other available knowledge, to estimate the true density of the Earth. This scenario and Cavendish's data will be used to illustrate the analysis of data from a normal model with unknown mean and variance.

Example 14.1 A model for Cavendish's data

Errors in experimental measurements are often modelled by a normal distribution, and there is no obvious reason why such a model would be inappropriate for Cavendish's measurements. Therefore it is reasonable to assume that Cavendish's measurements are a random sample of observations on a random variable X, where X has a normal distribution with mean μ, the true density of the Earth, and variance σ^2, that is,

$$X \sim N(\mu, \sigma^2).$$

An implicit assumption in this formulation is that Cavendish's measurements are unbiased.

Since the parameters μ and σ^2 of the normal distribution are unknown, beliefs about likely values can be expressed through a prior probability density function $f(\mu, \sigma^2)$. This p.d.f. is the joint prior probability density function for μ and σ^2.

How can such a prior p.d.f. be specified?   ◆

Conjugate analysis for a normal mean and variance

A conjugate analysis exists when data are modelled by a normal distribution with unknown mean and unknown variance. However, in practice, the model is usually formulated in terms of the precision of the normal distribution, rather than the variance. The precision τ is equal to the reciprocal of the variance: $\tau = \sigma^{-2}$. Thus the model can be written as

The normal/normal model described in Subsection 8.3 applies only when the variance σ^2 is known.

$$X \sim N(\mu, 1/\tau).$$

With two unknown parameters μ and τ, the prior distribution takes the form of a joint prior distribution with joint p.d.f. $f(\mu, \tau)$. Every joint p.d.f. can be written as the product of a marginal p.d.f. and a conditional p.d.f. The conjugate joint prior p.d.f. for μ and τ can be written in the form

$$f(\mu, \tau) = f(\tau) f(\mu | \tau).$$

Thus the joint prior p.d.f. can be written as a marginal p.d.f. for τ, multiplied by a conditional p.d.f. for μ given a value for τ. Note that before observing any data, the parameters μ and τ are not assumed to be independent.

It can be shown that the components of the conjugate joint prior distribution are as follows: a normal distribution for μ, conditional on the value of τ,

$$\mu|\tau \sim N(a, b/\tau),$$

where $-\infty < a < \infty$ and $b > 0$; and a gamma distribution for τ,

$$\tau \sim \text{Gamma}(c, d),$$

where $c, d > 0$. The joint prior distribution for μ and τ is called a **normal-gamma distribution**, and is denoted

$$\mu, \tau \sim \text{Ngamma}(a, b, c, d).$$

Given a random sample of size n from a normal distribution with unknown mean and unknown variance, the joint posterior distribution has the same normal-gamma form as the joint prior distribution, but with updated parameters:

$$\mu, \tau|\text{data} \sim \text{Ngamma}(A, B, C, D).$$

The conditional posterior distribution for μ and the marginal posterior distribution for τ have the same normal and gamma forms as their prior distributions, but with updated parameters, that is,

$$\mu|\tau, \text{data} \sim N(A, B/\tau),$$
$$\tau|\text{data} \sim \text{Gamma}(C, D).$$

In Subsection 8.3, you saw that when the variance (and hence the precision) is known, the conjugate prior distribution for μ takes the form of a normal distribution. When the precision τ is unknown, the *conditional* prior distribution for μ, given a particular value of τ, is also a normal distribution, but in this case the variance depends on the value of τ. For example, when τ increases, representing greater precision (or lower variance) in the model for the data, the variance of the prior distribution for μ decreases, reflecting more certain beliefs about the value of μ.

> In a Bayesian context, parameters have distributions, so it makes sense to describe them as dependent or independent.

> The formulas for the updated parameters have been omitted; you will not need them.

Activity 14.1   Does a conjugate prior reflect your prior beliefs?

A model for Cavendish's measurements on the density of the Earth was described in Example 14.1. If you believed that Cavendish's measurements were very accurate, in which case the value of the precision $\tau = \sigma^{-2}$ would be large, would this make you more certain about the value of μ, the true density of the Earth, than if you believed they were not very accurate?

A conjugate analysis will be performed on Cavendish's data in order to demonstrate a number of features of multi-parameter problems. The first thing to do is to specify the parameters a, b, c and d of the joint prior distribution for μ and τ. This is done in Example 14.2.

Example 14.2   Specifying a prior distribution

The marginal prior distribution for τ takes the form of a gamma distribution with parameters c and d, that is,

$$\tau \sim \text{Gamma}(c, d).$$

Suppose that Cavendish had determined from previous experiments that his measuring equipment was such that the variance of the measurements was most likely to be around 0.125, and very unlikely to be either greater than 0.5 or less than 0.025. Converting these beliefs into beliefs about the precision τ means that the most likely value for the precision is 8, and it is unlikely to be either less than 2 or greater than 40. If it is also assumed that $P(\tau < 2) \simeq 0.025$ and $P(\tau > 40) \simeq 0.025$, then it can be shown that a gamma distribution with parameters $c = 2.2$ and $d = 0.15$ reflects these beliefs quite well. For instance, for this distribution, the mode is 8 and

$$P(\tau < 2) \simeq 0.0238, \quad P(\tau > 40) \simeq 0.0233.$$

The p.d.f. of the Gamma(2.2, 0.15) distribution is shown in Figure 14.1.

There are two parameters to specify in the prior distribution for μ: the prior mean a, and the parameter b. The parameter a is fairly straightforward to assess, as it is the mean, median and mode of the prior distribution for μ. The parameter b is more complicated to specify, so the details of how this is done will be omitted.

Suppose that you do not know the mass or volume of the Earth, so that you cannot estimate the density of the Earth directly. Suppose also that you have only a basic appreciation of the chemical and geological composition of the Earth, and hence have little prior knowledge about the density of the Earth. In order to specify a prior for the value of the density of the Earth, some idea of the densities of various substances would be useful. The densities of nine commonly occurring substances are given in Table 14.1.

The Earth is almost certainly denser than water but less dense than iron, so it might be reasonable to assume that its true density is most likely to be roughly halfway between the densities of water and iron.

Thus, based on this information, we might assess the most likely value of μ to be 4, and believe that values less than 1 or greater than 7 are extremely unlikely.

With these beliefs it can be shown that a conditional prior distribution for μ is of the form

$$\mu | \tau \sim N(4, 7/\tau),$$

a normal distribution with mean $a = 4$ and variance b/τ, where $b = 7$. (You do not need to know how the parameter b was determined, only that it was not straightforward to obtain.) The p.d.f. of this prior distribution, conditional on the value $\tau = 8$, which is the prior mode of τ, is shown in Figure 14.2.

Therefore the joint prior distribution for μ and τ is

$$\mu, \tau \sim \text{Ngamma}(4, 7, 2.2, 0.15). \quad \blacklozenge$$

Having specified the prior, the next step is to obtain the data and perform the Bayesian analysis. This is done in Example 14.3.

The parameters c and d were determined using a method similar to that used by *LearnBayes*.

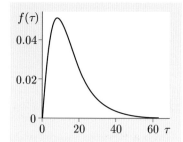

Figure 14.1 The Gamma(2.2, 0.15) density

Table 14.1 Densities of various substances

Substance	Density (g/cm^3)
Gold	19.30
Lead	11.34
Copper	8.92
Iron	7.87
Diamond	3.50
Aluminium	2.70
Water	1.00
Ethanol	0.79
Air	0.0012

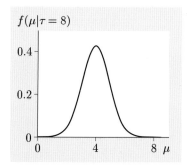

Figure 14.2 Prior for μ conditional on $\tau = 8$

Example 14.3 *The data and the posterior distribution*

The 29 measurements made by Cavendish are given in Table 14.2.

Table 14.2 Cavendish's measurements of the density of the Earth

5.50	5.61	4.88	5.07	5.26	5.55	5.36	5.29	5.58	5.65
5.57	5.53	5.62	5.29	5.44	5.34	5.79	5.10	5.27	5.39
5.42	5.47	5.63	5.34	5.46	5.30	5.75	5.68	5.85	

Stigler, S.M. (1977) Do robust estimators work with real data? *Annals of Statistics*, **5**, 1055–1098.

The sample mean and sample variance derived from these data are $\overline{x} = 5.447\,931 \simeq 5.45$ and $s^2 = 0.048\,817 \simeq 0.0488$.

For these data and the prior specified in Example 14.2, the conjugate analysis results in the following joint posterior distribution for μ and τ:

$$\mu, \tau | \text{data} \sim \text{Ngamma}(5.44, 0.0343, 16.7, 0.982).$$

This means that

$$\mu | \tau, \text{data} \sim N(5.44, 0.0343/\tau),$$
$$\tau | \text{data} \sim \text{Gamma}(16.7, 0.982).$$

These distributions can be used to make inferences about the unknown quantities μ and τ. ◆

The values of the parameters have been rounded to three significant figures. You do not need to know how the values were calculated.

14.2 Marginal distributions

Given a Bayesian model with more than one unknown parameter, interest lies not only in the joint posterior distribution for these unknown parameters, but also in the posterior distributions for the parameters considered separately, that is, in their marginal distributions. The marginal distribution for a parameter is the *unconditional* distribution for the parameter.

Example 14.4   Cavendish's data: marginal posterior distribution for τ

For the normal-gamma joint posterior distribution given in Example 14.3, the marginal posterior distribution for τ is Gamma$(16.7, 0.982)$. The corresponding marginal posterior density is shown in Figure 14.3 together with the marginal prior density.

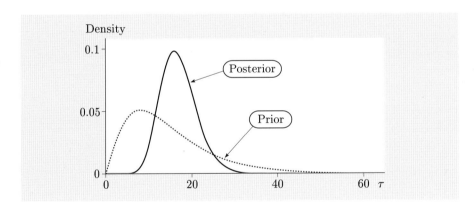

Figure 14.3   Marginal posterior density and marginal prior density for τ

Figure 14.3 illustrates the extent to which the data have updated the prior beliefs about the precision τ. The variance of the posterior distribution is smaller than the variance of the prior distribution. Also, before observing the data, the most likely value of τ was 8, but the mode of the posterior distribution is given by

$$\text{mode} = \frac{16.7 - 1}{0.982} \simeq 15.99.$$

The mode of Gamma(a, b) is $(a - 1)/b$.

An equal-tailed 95% credible interval for τ, computed directly from the properties of the gamma distribution, is $(9.85, 26.08)$. ◆

LearnBayes was used to calculate this interval.

As you have seen, study of the marginal posterior distribution for τ is straightforward. However, the quantity of primary interest from the analysis of Cavendish's measurements of the density of the Earth is the parameter μ — the mean of the normal model for the data. This represents the true density of the Earth.

Example 14.5 Cavendish's data: marginal posterior distribution for μ

In Example 14.3, you saw that the conditional posterior distribution for μ given a value of the precision τ is $N(5.44, 0.0343/\tau)$. The conditional posterior density for μ is shown in Figure 14.4(a) for three particular values of τ.

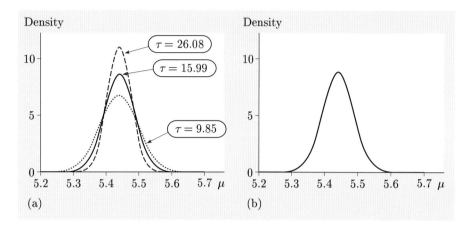

(a) (b)

Figure 14.4 (a) Conditional posterior density for μ, given $\tau = 9.85$, $\tau = 15.99$ and $\tau = 26.08$ (b) Marginal posterior density for μ

The three values of τ chosen for illustration in Figure 14.4(a) are the marginal posterior mode of τ (15.99), and the lower and upper limits of the equal-tailed 95% credible interval given in Example 14.4. Note that the posterior mean of μ is 5.44, whatever the value of τ, but the variance of the normal posterior distribution increases as the precision τ decreases.

If the correct value of τ were known, then it would be appropriate to condition on that value. But the value of τ is not known, so which value of τ is the most appropriate value to condition on? Should it be the most likely value of τ (the marginal posterior mode), or some other value?

Of course, given that τ is unknown, there is no single correct value of τ that would be appropriate. Since the value of τ is unknown, it is desirable to take into account all possible values of τ. This can be done by averaging the conditional posterior p.d.f. for μ over all values of τ to obtain the marginal p.d.f. for μ. Thus interest lies in the marginal posterior distribution for the parameter μ.

For the normal-gamma distribution, the marginal posterior distribution for μ can be determined exactly. The marginal posterior density for μ is shown in Figure 14.4(b). Comparing this density with the conditional p.d.f.s in Figure 14.4(a), it looks as though the marginal distribution might also be normal. In fact, it is not normal, but has the form of a standard probability distribution, called the **Student t-distribution**.

You are not expected to be familiar with t-distributions.

The marginal p.d.f. for μ encapsulates the information from your prior beliefs about likely values of the density of the Earth, and the information provided by Cavendish's experimental measurements. All the uncertainty in the other unknown model parameter τ has been taken into account when deriving this marginal distribution.

The marginal posterior mean of μ is the same as the mean of all the conditional posterior distributions for μ, that is, 5.44. Therefore an estimate of the density of the Earth, based on prior beliefs and on Cavendish's measurements, is $5.44\,\text{g/cm}^3$. An equal-tailed 95% credible interval for μ can be calculated directly from the marginal posterior for μ as $(5.35, 5.53)\,\text{g/cm}^3$. ◆

Activity 14.2   Updated beliefs about the density of the Earth

Figure 14.5 shows the marginal posterior density for μ together with the marginal prior density for μ.

This marginal prior distribution can be calculated mathematically in the same way as the marginal posterior distribution.

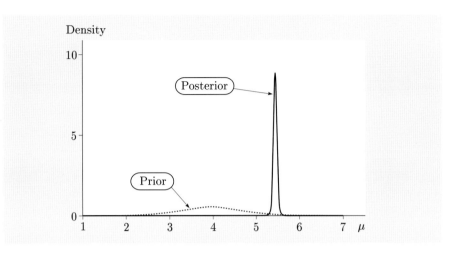

Figure 14.5   Marginal posterior density and marginal prior density for μ

In one or two sentences, describe the main ways in which the prior beliefs about μ, the density of the Earth, have been updated by the information in the data.

14.3   *Samples from joint distributions and marginal distributions*

The conjugate nature of the analysis of Cavendish's data allowed the marginal distribution for μ to be derived mathematically in the form of a standard probability distribution. However, this is often not possible. Fortunately, simulating from a marginal distribution is easy provided that you can simulate from the joint distribution. Simulation from joint distributions is discussed in this subsection.

Example 14.6   A conjugate analysis of Cavendish's data

In Example 14.1, a normal model with unknown mean and variance was suggested for Henry Cavendish's measurements of the density of the Earth:

$$X \sim N(\mu, 1/\tau),$$

where the precision τ is the reciprocal of the variance.

In Example 14.2, the following conjugate prior was specified for the unknown parameters μ and τ:

$$\mu, \tau \sim \text{Ngamma}(4, 7, 2.2, 0.15).$$

Given Cavendish's data, the joint posterior distribution for μ and τ is

$$\mu, \tau | \text{data} \sim \text{Ngamma}(5.44, 0.0343, 16.7, 0.982).$$

See Example 14.3.

Suppose that $N = 10\,000$ pairs of values (μ_i, τ_i), $i = 1, \ldots, N$, are sampled from this joint posterior distribution.

Simulation from this joint distribution is straightforward, but the details are omitted.

The natural way to display the simulation results is in a scatterplot. This shows the relationship between the two parameters and provides a representation of the form of the joint p.d.f.

The 10 000 simulated pairs of values from the joint posterior distribution based on Cavendish's data are shown in the scatterplot in Figure 14.6.

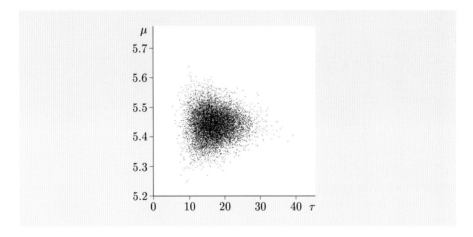

Figure 14.6 Scatterplot of simulated values from the joint posterior distribution for μ and τ

Since, in general, more values will be sampled from regions with high probability density, the regions in which the points are densely plotted correspond to regions where the p.d.f. takes relatively large values. The region with the largest probability density seems to be where τ is between 15 and 20, and μ is about 5.45. ◆

Activity 14.3 Interpreting a scatterplot

Use the scatterplot in Figure 14.6 to describe the main feature of the posterior relationship between the parameters μ and τ.

Another useful summary of the relationship between two quantities is provided by their correlation. The correlation between two quantities can be estimated by the sample correlation calculated from a sample of values from their joint distribution. For example, you may be interested in answering questions such as: 'Are two parameters in a Bayesian model highly correlated after observing the data?'

Example 14.7 Estimating the posterior correlation

The posterior correlation between the parameters μ and τ can be estimated from the sample correlation between the pairs sampled from the joint posterior distribution.

For the sample of 10 000 values reported in Example 14.6, the sample correlation is -0.003. This is very close to zero, which suggests that μ and τ are not (linearly) correlated in their posterior distribution. However, note that μ and τ are not independent in their posterior distribution: the variance of μ decreases as τ increases. This illustrates the general point that correlation is not the same as dependence. ◆

Deriving a marginal distribution from a joint distribution can be very complicated to do mathematically, since it involves averaging over the uncertainty about the other variables in the joint distribution. However, estimating marginal distributions based on simulated values from a joint distribution is straightforward. This is illustrated in Example 14.8.

Example 14.8 The marginal posterior distribution for μ

In the analysis of Cavendish's measurements of the density of the Earth, the quantity of primary interest is the parameter μ, the mean of the normal model for the data. This represents the true density of the Earth.

Given a sample of pairs of values (μ_i, τ_i), $i = 1, 2, \ldots, N$, from the joint posterior distribution, then the sample of values μ_i, $i = 1, 2, \ldots, N$, is a sample from the marginal posterior distribution for μ. Likewise, the sampled values of τ when considered separately from the sampled values of μ are a sample of values from the marginal posterior distribution for τ.

The relationships between joint and marginal distributions based on simulations is illustrated in Figure 14.7.

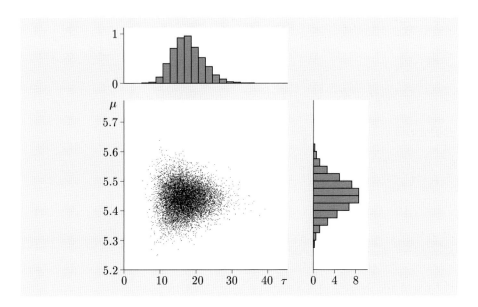

Figure 14.7 Scatterplot of 10 000 simulated values from the joint posterior distribution for μ and τ, and density histograms representing the marginal posterior densities for μ and τ

The sampled pairs of values of μ and τ are represented in the scatterplot. If only the value of μ in each pair is considered, then a density histogram of the values of μ can be constructed. This represents the marginal distribution for μ, and is shown in the right-hand 'margin' of the scatterplot. Similarly, considering only the values of τ in each pair leads to the density histogram in the top margin of the scatterplot. This represents the marginal distribution for τ.

The marginal posterior distribution for μ can be summarized by analysing the sampled values of μ — for example, by producing graphical and numerical summaries.

The density histogram of the simulated values of μ in the right-hand margin of Figure 14.7 is reproduced in Figure 14.8. This represents the marginal posterior p.d.f. for μ, $f(\mu|\text{data})$.

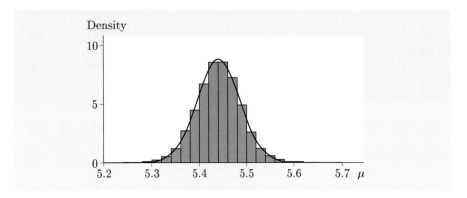

Figure 14.8   Density histogram of 10 000 simulated values from the marginal posterior distribution for μ, with exact marginal posterior p.d.f. overlaid

The distribution appears symmetric, centred on a value of μ of approximately $5.44\,\text{g/cm}^3$, and values less than $5.3\,\text{g/cm}^3$ or greater than $5.6\,\text{g/cm}^3$ are extremely unlikely. This posterior distribution encapsulates all the available information about the true value of the density of the Earth in 1798, based on prior beliefs and Cavendish's measurements.

An estimate of the posterior mean of μ (together with its MC error), calculated from the sampled values of μ, is 5.441 (4.68×10^{-4}). The estimated equal-tailed 95% credible interval for μ calculated from the simulated values is $(5.35, 5.54)$. These values are very similar to the values reported in Example 14.5.

The exact marginal posterior p.d.f. for μ is superimposed on the histogram in Figure 14.8. This is the p.d.f. that was shown in Figure 14.4(b). This demonstrates the validity of obtaining samples from a marginal distribution as a by-product of samples from a joint distribution.   ◆

In general, the exact form of a marginal distribution will not be available for comparison.

Activity 14.4   Drawing conclusions about the density of the Earth

At the time of writing, the accepted value of the density of the Earth is (approximately) $5.515\,\text{g/cm}^3$.

Is the information about the density of the Earth provided by the marginal posterior p.d.f. for μ obtained in Example 14.8 at odds with the current accepted value? If you think it is, then suggest two explanations for the discrepancy.

Summary of Section 14

In this section, Bayesian analysis of models with two parameters has been discussed. The normal model with unknown mean and variance has been introduced, and a conjugate analysis for the two unknown parameters has been described. This involved working with the joint posterior distribution for the parameters, and obtaining the marginal distributions.

You have learned that when dealing with a Bayesian model with more than one unknown parameter, the general principles of simulation apply. Samples from a bivariate joint distribution can be analysed using histograms of the marginal distributions and a scatterplot of the joint distribution, as well as numerical summaries such as means and credible intervals. Stochastic simulation provides an easy method of summarizing marginal distributions that would otherwise be too complicated to summarize mathematically. In particular, you have learned that when sampling from a joint distribution, the sampled values of a parameter form a sample from the marginal distribution for the parameter.

Exercise on Section 14

Exercise 14.1   *Marginal posterior distribution for the precision*

Figure 14.7 shows the scatterplot of 10 000 values simulated from the joint posterior distribution for μ and τ. Also shown are density histograms representing the marginal distributions of μ and τ.

(a) Use Figure 14.7 to obtain a rough estimate of the mode of the marginal posterior distribution for τ.

(b) The marginal posterior distribution for τ is Gamma(16.7, 0.982). Calculate the posterior mode of τ, and compare the mode with the estimate you obtained in part (a).

See Example 14.4.

15 Transformations and multivariate problems in practice

In this section, you will use WinBUGS to study the examples discussed in Sections 13 and 14.

Refer to Chapter 10 of Computer Book 4 for the work in this section.

Summary of Section 15

In this section, you have used WinBUGS to obtain samples from the posterior distribution for a function of one or more parameters, and to calculate summaries. You have also learned how to simulate from a posterior distribution involving more than one parameter, and how to summarize the results.

Part IV   Markov chain Monte Carlo

Introduction to Part IV

In Bayesian statistics, the posterior distribution is used to make inferences about the quantity (or quantities) of interest. This is straightforward when the posterior distribution is a standard distribution, as is the case for the conjugate analyses described in Part II, or when values from the posterior distribution can be simulated by sampling independent values from a standard probability distribution, as in Part III. However, when the posterior distribution is complicated, it may not be possible to calculate it mathematically or sample independent values from it directly. In such situations, a more general and more powerful simulation approach than that discussed in Part III, known as **Markov chain Monte Carlo**, can be used. Markov chain Monte Carlo, or MCMC for short, can deal with the task of sampling from (almost) any posterior distribution, no matter how complex. Unfortunately, this generality comes at a price, and special care needs to be taken when dealing with the sampled values.

In Section 16, the basic idea behind MCMC is discussed, and the use of WinBUGS to perform MCMC simulations is introduced. Some guidelines on how the simulated values from an MCMC simulation should be used for making inferences are given in Section 17. In Section 18, prior distributions for transformations of parameters are considered, and you will use WinBUGS to sample from posterior distributions for transformed parameters. Section 19 consists of a worked case study.

16 Markov chain Monte Carlo

In this section, a simulation method known as **Markov chain Monte Carlo**, or MCMC for short, is introduced. This method is perhaps the most general and widely applicable simulation strategy for sampling from complicated posterior distributions. The key difference between Markov chain Monte Carlo and the methods that were used in Part III is that the values sampled by MCMC are not independent. In fact, the values are sampled from what is known as a *Markov chain*. In Subsection 16.1, Markov chains and their simulation are discussed briefly. An example which illustrates how MCMC can be used for Bayesian inference is given in Subsection 16.2. When using MCMC for simulations from a posterior distribution involving two or more unknown parameters, values of each unknown parameter are sampled separately, so simulation from a complicated joint distribution is essentially replaced by several smaller, more manageable simulations. This aspect of MCMC is one of its great strengths. An example involving two parameters is described in Subsection 16.3, and you will use WinBUGS to carry out the analysis in Subsection 16.4.

16.1 Markov chains and their simulation

Essentially, a **Markov chain** is a sequence of random variables in which the distribution of the next random variable depends on the value of the current random variable, but is independent of the values of all previous random variables. Markov chains will not be defined formally, and their theory will not be considered in this book. However, Markov chains are of interest here because simulation from a Markov chain is straightforward. All that is required is an **initial value** from which to start the simulation, and a **transition rule** for generating the next value in the sequence, conditional on the current value.

Two properties that are characteristic of simulations from Markov chains, and which are a consequence of the dependent nature of a sample of values from a Markov chain, are illustrated in Example 16.1.

Example 16.1 A simulated Markov chain

Figure 16.1 shows 500 values $x_1, x_2, \ldots, x_{500}$ simulated from a Markov chain.

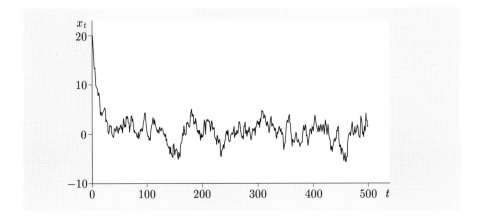

Figure 16.1 First 500 values simulated from a Markov chain

The initial value for the simulation was $x_1 = 20$. In Figure 16.1, the simulated values x_t are plotted against t, and the points are joined by lines. In Markov chain simulation, a plot such as this is sometimes referred to as a **trace plot**, as it traces the path of the Markov chain through time. Note that 'time' here refers to the ordered nature of the Markov chain simulation. Since the values are generated iteratively, it is common to refer to t as the **iteration**, or **iteration number**, rather than time.

Two features are evident from the trace plot in Figure 16.1. First, after the first 50 to 100 iterations, the sampled values appear to oscillate randomly around a constant mean with constant variance. That is, the sampled values appear to settle down in the sense that after an initial period, they look like values that have been sampled from the same distribution. Secondly, successive values are generally close, that is, they are quite highly correlated.   ♦

The two features of the simulation in Example 16.1 that were observed are characteristic of Markov chains. The first feature, that of settling down, so that all the values appear to be sampled from the same distribution, is known as **convergence**. Convergence is critical for the success of Markov chain Monte Carlo. The distribution from which the values are sampled after the values settle down is called the **equilibrium distribution**. The period before the values settle down is called the **transient period** or **transient phase**. The second feature, that successive values are generally close, arises because the values are generated iteratively, each value depending on the preceding value: the values are not sampled independently.

Alternative names for equilibrium distributions are stationary, or invariant, distributions.

16.2   Using MCMC for Bayesian inference

The idea behind using Markov chain Monte Carlo for Bayesian inference is as follows. If a Markov chain can be constructed so that its equilibrium distribution is the posterior distribution of interest, then the simulated values from the Markov chain, once they have settled down, can be treated as a sample of values from the posterior distribution. The fact that such a Markov chain can be constructed, and simulated values can be obtained from the Markov chain even when it is not possible to sample directly from the posterior distribution, makes MCMC a valuable tool for Bayesian inference.

There are essentially three steps involved in using MCMC for Bayesian inference.

◇   Set up a Markov chain that has the posterior distribution as its equilibrium distribution.

◇   Sample from the Markov chain.

◇   Use the sampled values (from the equilibrium distribution) to make inferences about the unknown quantities of interest.

There are several technical aspects involved in setting up an appropriate Markov chain. Fortunately, WinBUGS takes care of these: given the data, a model for the data and a prior, WinBUGS sets up a Markov chain whose equilibrium distribution is the posterior distribution of interest.

There are also many technical aspects of Markov chains, and in particular, conditions which are required for a Markov chain to have an equilibrium distribution. These will not be discussed: you can assume that the conditions needed for convergence will be met by the Markov chains in this course. Only the practical aspects of using MCMC for Bayesian inference will be discussed.

When sampling values, an assessment needs to be made about when convergence to the equilibrium distribution has occurred. This is usually done by visual inspection of trace plots. This aspect will be discussed in more detail in Section 17.

The values sampled from the Markov chain (once convergence to the equilibrium distribution has taken place) can be used for making inferences in the same way as for independent samples. The one complicating feature is that the dependence of the sampled values needs to be taken into account when computing the Monte Carlo standard error (MC error). The details of how this is done will not be considered here. All you need to know is that the estimated MC errors reported by WinBUGS allow for the dependence between the sampled values.

Example 16.2   MCMC-based inference about the Borel parameter

Data on the sizes of platoons of vehicles on a section of the Trans-Canada Highway, in Western Canada, were introduced in Section 10. A Borel(θ) model was proposed for the data, and a beta prior was suggested for the parameter θ. In Example 10.2, you saw that the p.d.f. of the resulting posterior is not that of a standard probability distribution.

See Examples 10.1 and 10.2.

MCMC can be used to sample from the posterior distribution by simulating values from a Markov chain which has the posterior distribution as its equilibrium distribution.

MCMC was used to simulate a sample of $N = 10\,000$ values from the equilibrium distribution of such a Markov chain. The sampled values, which represent a (dependent) sample from the posterior distribution for θ, can be used for making inferences about θ.

Figure 16.2 shows a density histogram of the simulated values. This histogram represents an estimate of the posterior p.d.f. $f(\theta|\text{data})$.

Estimates of the posterior mean, standard deviation and median of θ, based on the sampled values, are 0.425, 0.027 and 0.425, respectively, and an estimate of the equal-tailed 95% posterior credible interval for θ is $(0.376, 0.477)$.   ♦

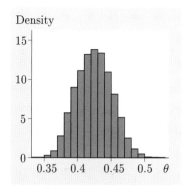

Figure 16.2   Density histogram of 10 000 values sampled from the posterior distribution for θ

Activity 16.1   Interpreting posterior beliefs about θ

The prior Beta$(2.9, 8.6)$ was chosen to reflect an expert's belief that the most likely value is around 0.2, and that the probability that θ is between 0.1 and 0.6 is about 0.9. The posterior density, as estimated from the MCMC sample in Example 16.2, and the Beta$(2.9, 8.6)$ prior density for the Borel parameter θ are shown in Figure 16.3.

See Activity 10.1 and Example 10.2.

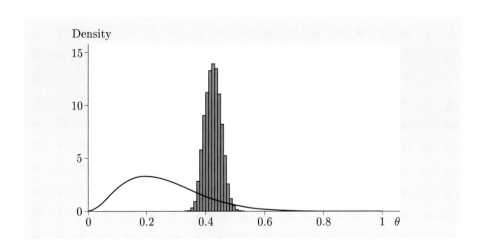

Figure 16.3   Prior density and estimate of posterior density for θ

Describe the main ways in which the traffic expert's prior beliefs about the traffic intensity parameter θ have been updated by the data.

In Example 16.2, you may have noticed that the Monte Carlo standard error was not reported after the mean estimate. Since the sampled values are not independent, special methods are required to estimate the MC error. WinBUGS calculates an estimate of the MC error which accounts for possible dependence in the sampled values. In all subsequent computations, the estimate of the MC error given will have taken any dependence into account.

16.3   Independent prior distributions

When faced with a model with two or more unknown parameters, it is generally hard to specify the joint prior distribution for the parameters directly. An alternative is to specify independent marginal prior distributions for each of the unknown parameters. For example, if the unknown parameters are $\theta_1, \theta_2, \ldots, \theta_p$, then the joint prior p.d.f. is the product of the independent marginal prior p.d.f.s:

$$f(\theta_1, \theta_2, \ldots, \theta_p) = f(\theta_1) \times f(\theta_2) \times \cdots \times f(\theta_p).$$

Quite often in such cases, a conjugate analysis is not possible. However, MCMC can be used to sample from the resulting posterior distribution.

Note that although the parameters $\theta_1, \theta_2, \ldots, \theta_p$ are independent in their prior distributions, they are not necessarily independent in their posterior distributions. That is, the posterior distribution may indicate that the parameters are not independent.

The use of independent priors is illustrated in Example 16.3.

Example 16.3   Determining the density of the Earth

In Section 14, Henry Cavendish's experimental measurements on the density of the Earth were discussed. It was assumed that Cavendish's measurements $x_1, x_2, \ldots, x_{29}$ are a random sample of observations on a random variable X, where X has a normal distribution with unknown mean μ, the true density of the Earth, and precision τ, that is,

$$X \sim N(\mu, 1/\tau).$$

A conjugate normal-gamma prior was chosen, primarily for simplicity of calculation. Perhaps the main difficulty with this prior is specifying values for its parameters. This is difficult when the distributions of the mean and precision are dependent. It is much easier to express beliefs about unknown quantities independently of one another.

Instead of a normal-gamma joint prior $\mathrm{Ngamma}(a, b, c, d)$, assume independent normal and gamma priors, for μ and τ, respectively:

$$\mu \sim N(a, b),$$
$$\tau \sim \mathrm{Gamma}(c, d).$$

This says that μ is modelled by a normal distribution with mean a and variance b, and that τ is modelled by a gamma distribution with parameters c and d.

In the conjugate analysis that was described in Section 14, the marginal prior distribution for τ was also a gamma distribution. Since the beliefs about the value of τ have not changed, it makes sense to choose the parameters of the gamma distribution to be the same as those chosen in Example 14.2. These beliefs were that the most likely value of τ was around 8, and that values of τ less than 2 or greater than 40 were very unlikely. These beliefs were reflected by the prior

$$\tau \sim \mathrm{Gamma}(2.2, 0.15),$$

that is, using $c = 2.2$ and $d = 0.15$.

Since independent priors are being assumed for μ and τ, a marginal prior distribution must be specified for μ, rather than a conditional prior distribution (as was the case in the conjugate analysis).

The beliefs about μ that were expressed in Example 14.2 were that the most likely value of μ is around 4, and that values less than 1 or greater than 7 are extremely unlikely. Since, for a normal distribution, values more than three standard deviations from the mean are very unlikely to occur, a prior distribution for μ that reflects these beliefs is a normal distribution with mean $a = 4$ and variance $b = 1$:

See Subsection 5.1.

$$\mu \sim N(4, 1).$$

In Example 14.2, it was observed that the specification of the parameter b in the conditional prior distribution $N(a, b/\tau)$ for μ is not easy. The specification of the parameter b in the marginal prior distribution for μ is much easier, since the value of τ does not come into the specification.

With this prior, the posterior distribution does not have the same form as the prior distribution. The joint prior density, which is the product of the independent normal and gamma priors for μ and τ, is not a conjugate prior, and the posterior distribution does not have a simple form.

Direct simulation from the posterior distribution is not possible. Fortunately, a Markov chain can be constructed that has the joint posterior distribution for μ and τ as its equilibrium distribution. Simulating values from this Markov chain is one method that can be used to make posterior inferences. Note that here the simulated Markov chain is for two parameters, μ and τ. You will use WinBUGS to simulate values from this Markov chain in Subsection 16.4.   ♦

16.4   Markov chain simulation in practice

In this subsection, you will use WinBUGS to simulate values from the posterior distribution for the model described in Subsection 16.3 using MCMC.

Refer to Chapter 11 of Computer Book 4 for the work in this subsection.

Summary of Section 16

In this section, the basic idea behind Markov chain Monte Carlo has been discussed. Trace plots have been introduced. These are plots of the simulated values against iteration number. Two properties of Markov chains have been noted. First, the distribution of the sampled values from a Markov chain settles down to a distribution called the equilibrium distribution. Secondly, the values in the chain are not independent. In MCMC, a Markov chain is constructed whose equilibrium distribution is the posterior distribution of interest in a Bayesian analysis. The simulated values of the Markov chain can be used for making inferences. You have seen that the use of independent priors for the parameters of a model involving more than one parameter may result in a posterior which is not a standard probability distribution. You have learned how to use WinBUGS to carry out MCMC for the situation where independent priors are specified for the parameters of the normal model with unknown mean μ and precision τ.

17   Dealing with samples from MCMC

In this section, a standard procedure for MCMC simulation is discussed. This involves choosing initial values, assessing when the sequence of simulated values has converged to the equilibrium distribution, and deciding which of the simulated values to use for making inferences.

The procedure that is generally recommended is summarized in the following box.

Standard procedure for MCMC

◇   Run a small number of separate simulations, say three to five, each started from a different initial value. The initial values are simulated from the prior distribution.

◇   For each parameter in the model, inspect trace plots of the simulated values of the parameter from all the simulations. Hence assess when it is safe to assume that convergence to the equilibrium distribution has been reached.

◇   Discard the sampled values that are deemed to come from the transient phase of the Markov chain simulation.

◇   Use the remaining sampled values for producing graphical and numerical summaries of the parameters of interest.

Note that, strictly speaking, convergence of a sequence of simulated values to the equilibrium distribution of the Markov chain is guaranteed only after an infinite number of iterations. However, when dealing with sampled values obtained using MCMC, what is actually required is practical convergence. This is reached when the sampled values are indistinguishable from those from the equilibrium distribution.

This procedure will be illustrated for the model and data described in Example 17.1.

Example 17.1   Modelling the catch of South Atlantic albacore tuna

Table 17.1 contains data on the annual catch in thousands of tonnes of South Atlantic albacore tuna for each of the 23 years from 1967 to 1989.

Table 17.1   Catch of albacore tuna (thousands of tonnes)

15.9	25.7	28.5	23.7	25.0	33.3	28.2	19.7
17.5	19.3	21.6	23.1	22.5	22.5	23.6	29.1
14.4	13.2	28.4	34.6	37.5	25.9	25.3	

Millar, R.B. (2004) Sensitivity of Bayes estimators to hyper-parameters with an application to maximum yield from fisheries. *Biometrics*, **60**, 536–542.

A histogram of the data is shown in Figure 17.1.

Let X represent the catch, in thousands of tonnes, in a year. An appropriate model for the data is a normal model with unknown mean and variance:

$$X \sim N(\mu, \sigma^2).$$

The standard deviation σ is constrained to be positive. In Example 14.2, a gamma prior was specified for $1/\sigma^2$. Here an alternative approach will be taken. It is quite common to transform constrained parameters so that the transformed parameter is defined for all real values. This gives extra flexibility when specifying prior beliefs. The transformation of the standard deviation using the logarithm function allows a prior distribution for $\log \sigma$ that is defined on the whole real line. A commonly used prior distribution is one in which μ and $\log \sigma$ are assigned normal distributions independently, that is,

$$\mu \sim N(a, b),$$
$$\log \sigma \sim N(c, d),$$

for some parameters a, b, c and d which must be specified.

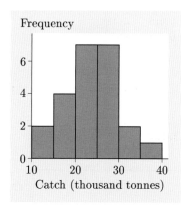

Figure 17.1   Histogram of catch of albacore tuna

Weak prior distributions will be used here to represent a lack of information about μ and $\log \sigma$. This is done by assigning very high variances to the normal prior distributions so that the priors are nearly flat over a large range of values — for example, normal distributions with mean zero and variance 100 might be used. That is,

$$\mu \sim N(0, 100),$$
$$\log \sigma \sim N(0, 100).$$

An obvious problem with this prior specification is that the catch must be non-negative, by definition. This prior implies that the mean catch is just as likely to be negative as it is to be positive. You would be quite right to question the validity of this prior for μ, but for the time being just accept it as a representation of ignorance by someone who thinks that the catch can take any value.

The posterior distribution is complicated, so one way to make inferences about the parameters μ and σ is to use MCMC to sample from the joint posterior distribution for μ and $\log \sigma$.   ◆

Choice of initial values

In the first step in the standard procedure, a small number of simulations are run, each with different initial values, which must be chosen in some way. Whatever initial values are used, the simulated values will eventually settle down so that, after a transient phase, they can be deemed to come from the equilibrium distribution of the Markov chain. Nevertheless, it is worth choosing the initial values sensibly.

The most widely used approach to choosing initial values is to simulate initial values from the prior distribution. Alternatively, in the unlikely event that it is difficult to simulate initial values from the prior distribution, it is usual practice to choose initial values that have a high prior probability, such as the prior mean or mode.

Example 17.2   Albacore tuna: initial values

Suppose that three simulations are to be run of a Markov chain which has the posterior distribution for μ and $\log \sigma$ as its equilibrium distribution. Then three pairs of initial values of μ and $\log \sigma$ are required. These can be sampled independently from the prior distributions for μ and $\log \sigma$.   ◆

Activity 17.1   Alternative initial values

If obtaining initial values by sampling from the prior distribution was not straightforward, suggest a set of initial values of μ and $\log \sigma$ to use for one of the three simulations. Justify your answer.

Assessing convergence

Convergence to the equilibrium distribution is assessed by inspecting trace plots of the simulated values. In practice, only lack of convergence can be assessed. In general, when convergence is reported, what is actually being reported is practical convergence, or no evidence to suggest lack of convergence.

The values sampled from a simulation that has converged oscillate around a constant mean with constant variance. Trace plots for simulations from two Markov chains are shown in Figure 17.2 (overleaf).

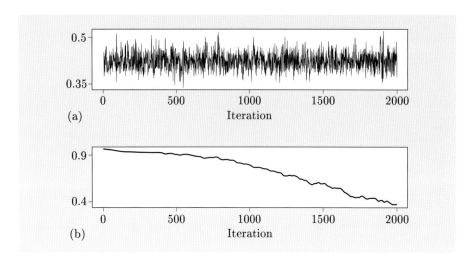

Figure 17.2   (a) No evidence against convergence (b) Clear evidence against convergence

The trace plot in Figure 17.2(a) shows no evidence of lack of convergence, whereas that in Figure 17.2(b) shows clear evidence of lack of convergence.

Evidence of lack of convergence is rarely as clear-cut as in Figure 17.2(b). Indeed, assessing practical convergence is more of an art than a science.

When assessing convergence it is advisable to err on the side of caution. Also, it is sensible to run the simulations for a large number of iterations initially, say $N = 10\,000$. Choosing too short an initial run can lead to incorrect conclusions being drawn. This is illustrated in Example 17.3.

Example 17.3   Albacore tuna: misleading results

Three simulations of a Markov chain which has the posterior distribution for μ and $\log \sigma$ as its equilibrium distribution were run for $N = 10\,000$ iterations. Figure 17.3 shows a trace plot of the first 700 values of μ from one of the simulations.

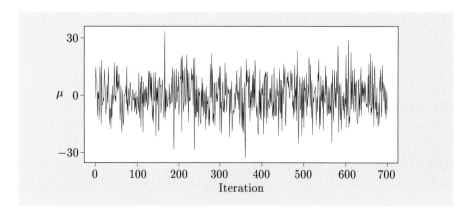

Figure 17.3   Trace plot of the first 700 simulated values of μ

To all intents and purposes this displays no evidence of lack of convergence. Now look at Figure 17.4, which shows trace plots of all 10 000 simulated values of μ and $\log \sigma$ for each of the three simulations.

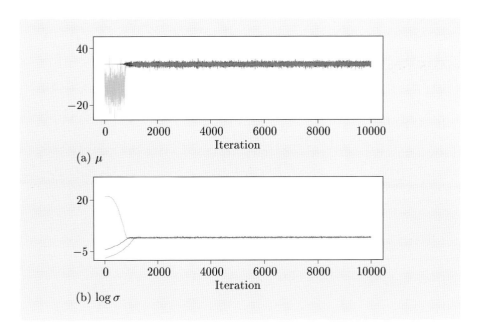

Figure 17.4 Trace plots of values from three simulations: (a) μ (b) $\log \sigma$

From Figure 17.4(a), it is clear that the first 700 values of the simulation shown in Figure 17.3 were in fact from the transient phase, before convergence is reached. ◆

Activity 17.2 Assessing convergence

Based on the trace plots in Figure 17.4, after which iteration m is there no longer any evidence of lack of convergence? Justify your answer.

Notice that in Figure 17.4, the trace plots for the three simulations have been superimposed on the same diagram. This makes it easier to assess practical convergence: if the simulations for a parameter do not overlap, then convergence has not yet been reached. In equilibrium, the values from the three simulations must overlap because they are sampled from the same distribution. Also notice that trace plots were produced for both μ and $\log \sigma$, as practical convergence cannot be deemed to have been reached as long as the trace plots for either parameter display evidence of lack of convergence.

In Example 17.3, you saw that it is all too easy to conclude incorrectly that practical convergence has been reached. In order to reduce the risk of doing this, the following guidelines should be observed when assessing convergence.

◇ Run more than one simulation: a small number k should be run, say three to five.

◇ Run the simulations for a large number of values, say $N = 10\,000$.

◇ For each parameter, produce trace plots of all the simulations, superimposed on the same diagram.

Practical convergence has not been reached if the simulations for a parameter do not overlap, or if the trace plots for any of the parameters display evidence of lack of convergence (such as changes in the mean and variance of the simulated values).

Several other methods are commonly used for assessing convergence. These are often called **convergence diagnostics**. These methods fall into three general categories: graphical methods, numerical methods, and a combination of both graphical and numerical methods. The methods also range from the informal to the mathematically sophisticated. These other methods will not be discussed in this book. Inspecting trace plots of simulated values is arguably the best informal way to diagnose lack of convergence.

Dealing with the sampled values

If the sampled values from the transient phase were included in the final sample used for making inferences, they might distort the inferences. Therefore the sampled values from the transient phase are discarded, and ignored in subsequent analysis. Only the sampled values from the equilibrium phase of a simulation should be used for making inferences.

The transient phase of a Markov chain simulation — that is, the phase before equilibrium is reached — is often referred to as the **burn-in** period. The term 'burn-in' is borrowed from electronics where it refers to the testing of electrical components. The components that have not failed after a certain length of testing are deemed to be worthy of general use; the idea is to eliminate the worst-performing components. The analogy with MCMC is not perfect, but the term 'burn-in' has become well-established.

Suppose that after iteration m there is no evidence of lack of convergence. Then iterations $1, 2, \ldots, m$ are ignored or discarded in all subsequent analysis. Only the sampled values at iterations $m + 1, m + 2, \ldots$ are used for making inferences.

Example 17.4 Albacore tuna: burn-in verification

In Activity 17.2, it was suggested that there was no evidence of lack of convergence after 2000 iterations. Therefore the first $m = 2000$ iterations are deemed to come from the transient, or burn-in period, and should be ignored. This is illustrated in Figure 17.5.

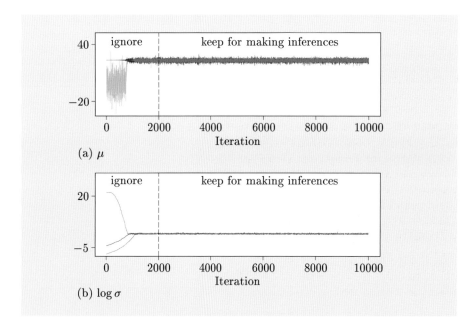

Figure 17.5 Trace plots of simulated values: (a) μ (b) $\log \sigma$ ◆

After the burn-in iterations have been discarded, trace plots of the remaining simulated values should be produced in order to verify that enough iterations have been discarded. If the remaining sampled values do not look as if they have converged, then more iterations should be discarded.

Trace plots of the values μ and $\log\sigma$ for the three simulations, ignoring the first $m = 2000$ iterations, are shown in Figure 17.6.

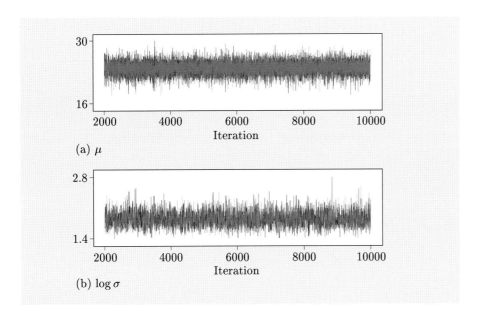

(a) μ

(b) $\log\sigma$

Figure 17.6   Trace plots of simulated values after ignoring the first 2000 iterations: (a) μ (b) $\log\sigma$

These trace plots do not provide any evidence of lack of convergence to the equilibrium distribution.

Inference

The Monte Carlo standard error was introduced in Part III to provide a measure of the accuracy of inferences based on simulations. The 5% rule of thumb can be useful for deciding whether sufficient sampled values have been obtained. This states that the MC error should be less than about 5% of the sample standard deviation. For MCMC, successive values are dependent; this has the effect of increasing the MC error. Estimating the MC error for MCMC is done by WinBUGS, so the details will not be given here. The main point to note is that, in general, to obtain a specified degree of accuracy, longer simulations may be needed with MCMC than with independent sampling. A second reason for running longer simulations is that values from the burn-in period must be discarded before using the sampled values for inference, thus reducing the number of values that can be used. Choosing the number of iterations in a simulation will not be discussed further: for all the simulations you will meet in this course, $N = 10\,000$ will be sufficient.

Example 17.5   Albacore tuna: inference

The first 2000 values in each of the three simulations of 10 000 values were discarded. Inferences were based on the remaining 24 000 values. Graphical summaries of these sampled values from the posterior distribution can be used for making inferences. The scatterplot in Figure 17.7(a) (overleaf) shows the posterior relationship between μ and $\log\sigma$.

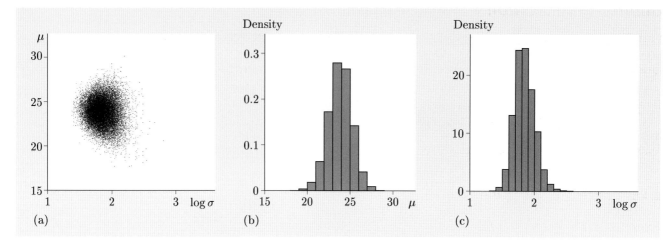

Figure 17.7   Simulated values of μ and $\log \sigma$: (a) scatterplot (b) density histogram for μ (c) density histogram for $\log \sigma$

Although the prior reflected the belief that the parameters μ and $\log \sigma$ are independent, μ and $\log \sigma$ may not in fact be independent. In the scatterplot, the variance of the values of μ appears to increase as the value of $\log \sigma$ increases. This suggests that μ and $\log \sigma$ may not be independent.

The density histograms in Figures 17.7(b) and 17.7(c) represent estimates of the marginal posterior densities of μ and $\log \sigma$, respectively. Comparing these estimated marginal posterior densities with the marginal prior densities is a good way to compare prior and posterior beliefs. This is done in Figure 17.8.

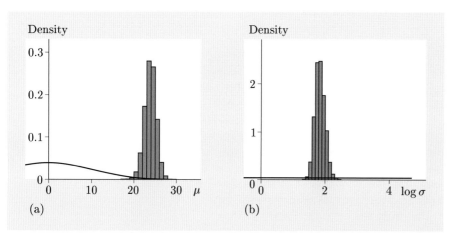

Figure 17.8   Prior density and density histogram representing marginal posterior density: (a) μ (b) $\log \sigma$

Notice how different the posterior is from the prior in each case: the weak prior information has been overwhelmed by information from the data.

The marginal posterior distributions summarize all the information available about the parameters. The graphical summaries in Figure 17.7 can be supplemented by numerical summaries. For example, using the estimated marginal posterior distribution for μ, an estimate of the mean catch μ is 23.84 (0.0088), and an estimate of the equal-tailed 90% credible interval for μ is (21.59, 26.04).   ◆

The MC error quoted in brackets, which was estimated by WinBUGS, takes the dependence of successive values into account.

Activity 17.3   Interpreting results

The annual catch of albacore tuna cannot be negative, but according to the prior, the probability that the mean catch is negative is 0.5. Does Figure 17.8(a) provide any evidence to suggest that the choice of prior distribution for μ has had a significant effect on the posterior inferences about μ? Justify your answer.

Summary of Section 17

In this section, several aspects of the practical implementation of MCMC have been described. These include the choice of initial values and the assessment of convergence to the equilibrium distribution. You have seen that in order to assess convergence, several simulations should be run. Trace plots of the simulated values for all the parameters are inspected for evidence of lack of convergence. The period before the simulations are deemed to have converged is called the burn-in period. Sampled values from the burn-in period are discarded, and the remaining values are used for making inferences about the parameters of interest.

Exercises on Section 17

Exercise 17.1   Priors for the South Atlantic albacore tuna

In Example 17.1, it was suggested that a normal model with unknown mean and variance is appropriate for data on the annual catch of South Atlantic albacore tuna:

$$X \sim N(\mu, \sigma^2).$$

The following weak normal priors were specified for μ and $\log \sigma$:

$$\mu \sim N(0, 100),$$
$$\log \sigma \sim N(0, 100).$$

However, the values of μ should ideally be restricted to be non-negative. Suggest a prior for μ, which also has variance 100 (to indicate lack of strong beliefs), that satisfies this requirement. Does the prior you have selected result in a conjugate analysis?

Exercise 17.2   Convergence assessment

Figure 17.9 shows trace plots of the sampled values from three simulations of a Markov chain, each with a different starting value. The Markov chain was constructed so that its equilibrium distribution is the posterior distribution for the unknown quantity θ.

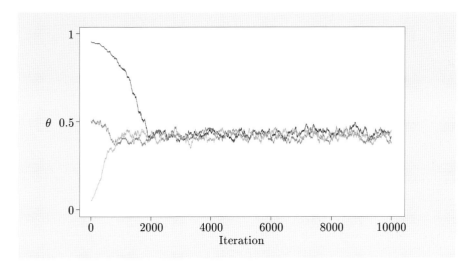

Figure 17.9   Trace plots of simulated values from three simulations

Based on these trace plots, what would you deem to be a suitable burn-in period? Justify your answer.

18 Practical implementation of MCMC

In this section, you will use WinBUGS to implement the standard procedure for MCMC simulation that was described in Section 17. You will analyse two data sets. The Bayesian models both involve specifying a prior for a transformation of a parameter, rather than the parameter itself.

When a parameter in a Bayesian model is constrained to be positive, or to lie in the interval $(0, 1)$, it is common practice to transform it so that the transformed parameter is unrestricted in the values it can take. This was done in Example 17.1 when specifying a prior for the parameters of a normal model with unknown mean and variance: a prior was specified for $\log \sigma$ instead of σ.

Another example of specifying a prior for a transformation of a parameter is described in Example 18.1.

Example 18.1   An alternative prior for the Borel parameter

Data on the sizes of 402 platoons of vehicles, recorded on a section of the Trans-Canada Highway, in Western Canada, were introduced in Example 10.1. A Borel distribution with parameter θ, where $0 < \theta < 1$, was proposed for the data; that is,

The data are in Table 10.1.

$$X \sim \text{Borel}(\theta),$$

where X is the size of a platoon.

To complete the Bayesian model, a prior for the unknown parameter θ is required. In Example 10.2, a beta prior for θ was specified; and an analysis using MCMC was described in Subsection 16.2.

Since the parameter θ is constrained to lie between 0 and 1, an alternative approach is to transform θ so that the transformed parameter can take any value on the whole real line.

A suitable transformation to consider is the **logit** transformation. For a quantity θ defined on the interval $(0, 1)$, the logit of θ is defined by

The logit is also known as the log odds.

$$\text{logit}(\theta) = \log\left(\frac{\theta}{1 - \theta}\right).$$

If θ can take any value between 0 and 1, then $\text{logit}(\theta)$ can take any value between $-\infty$ and ∞.

A suitable prior for $\text{logit}(\theta)$ is one which is defined on $(-\infty, \infty)$, such as a normal distribution.

If you had strong beliefs about likely values of $\text{logit}(\theta)$, then these could and should be used. However, it is also of interest to investigate what happens when the prior reflects a lack of strong prior beliefs about the value of $\text{logit}(\theta)$.

Weak prior beliefs can be expressed through a normal distribution with mean zero and large variance, for example,

$$\text{logit}(\theta) \sim N(0, 100^2).$$

With this prior, the complete Bayesian model is

$$X \sim \text{Borel}(\theta),$$
$$\text{logit}(\theta) \sim N(0, 100^2). \quad \blacklozenge$$

The second Bayesian model that you will analyse involves a parameter which is constrained to be positive. This is described in Example 18.2.

Example 18.2   Lung cancer in Finland

In a study of the effects of asbestos mining on the incidence of lung cancer, data were collected on the number of people with lung cancer in each of 47 regions surrounding an asbestos mine in Paakkila in the eastern part of Finland. The data are in Table 18.1.

Kokki, E. and Penttinen, A. (2003) Poisson regression with change-point prior in the modelling of disease risk around a point source. *Biometrical Journal*, **45**, 689–703.

Table 18.1   Lung cancer incidence in Paakkila, Finland

10	1	0	2	4	2	2	7	19	10	11	12
10	5	2	1	2	3	2	3	2	3	2	1
2	1	2	1	3	0	6	4	3	1	0	1
0	2	2	1	1	0	1	0	1	1	4	

The standard model for count data such as these is the Poisson distribution. If X represents the number of lung cancer cases in a region, then a model for the data is

$$X \sim \text{Poisson}(\lambda),$$

where $\lambda > 0$. Since the parameter λ cannot be negative, a possible prior for λ is a gamma distribution; this is the conjugate prior. Alternatively, since $\log \lambda$ can take any value, positive, negative or zero, a normal prior could be specified for $\log \lambda$.

Suppose that an expert believes that the most likely value of λ is 5, and that the probability that λ is greater than 10 is 0.05, or equivalently that the most likely value of $\log \lambda$ is $\log 5$, and the probability that $\log \lambda$ is greater than $\log 10$ is 0.05. These beliefs about $\log \lambda$ are reflected by a normal distribution with mean $\log 5 \simeq 1.61$ and variance 0.421^2; that is,

$$\log \lambda \sim N(1.61, 0.421^2). \quad \blacklozenge$$

Refer to Chapter 12 of Computer Book 4 for the rest of the work in this section.

Summary of Section 18

In this section, you have learned how to use WinBUGS to carry out a Bayesian analysis using the standard procedure for MCMC simulation that was described in Section 17. In the two Bayesian models that you analysed, a prior was specified for a transformation of a parameter. This was done so that the values that the transformed parameter could take were unconstrained.

19   Magnesium and myocardial infarction: a case study

In this section, you will work through a real life case study. The case study highlights some of the components of a full Bayesian analysis, as well as the usefulness of incorporating expert prior beliefs into an analysis.

The background to the case study is described in Subsection 19.1. A non-Bayesian analysis is described in Subsection 19.2, and a Bayesian model for the data is presented in Subsection 19.3. In Subsection 19.4, you will use WinBUGS to carry out an analysis of the data using this Bayesian model. Subsection 19.5 contains a brief discussion of the results. No new ideas or techniques are introduced in this section.

19.1 Magnesium and myocardial infarction: background

For many years it has been suspected that magnesium, taken intravenously, has an effect on patients with acute myocardial infarction (MI). Studies in animals and humans have suggested a protective effect. That is, subjects who were administered magnesium experienced a reduced risk of mortality.

A myocardial infarction is commonly known as a heart attack.

Over the years a number of studies have been undertaken to quantify the effect of magnesium on patients with myocardial infarction. In Subsection 19.4, you will use WinBUGS to analyse data from eight clinical trials that were performed before 1993. An analysis of the results of several clinical trials such as this is known as a meta-analysis. This simply means an analysis of several analyses.

The eight clinical trials were mostly small scale, involving only a few hundred patients. Data are also available from a much larger trial, known as a mega-trial, involving many thousands of patients. The results of this mega-trial, which involved a total of 58 050 patients, were published in 1995. The number of patients in the mega-trial is greater than the combined total number of patients in the eight smaller trials.

A non-Bayesian analysis of the first eight trials, using conventional methods, suggested that magnesium had a protective effect on patients with myocardial infarction, and that this effect was fairly strong. However, a non-Bayesian analysis of the data from the mega-trial suggested that there is no evidence of any effect.

The non-Bayesian analysis of the first eight trials is discussed briefly in Subsection 19.2.

This conflict between the results of the early trials and the mega-trial has provoked a great deal of debate by scientists working in this area. How could the results be so discrepant?

As well as the data from the trials, some expert opinion is available. Retrospectively, that is, after seeing the results of the mega-trial, one of the scientists involved with the original eight trials suggested that large effects were not to be expected, and stated that

> if one assumed that only moderate sized effects were possible, the apparent large effects observed in the meta-analyses of the small trials ... should perhaps have been tempered by this general judgement. If a result appears too good to be true, it probably is.

This scepticism about large effects was echoed by other scientists working in this area.

In this case study, you will investigate whether a Bayesian analysis of the data from the first eight trials, using a prior which reflects the experts' sceptical beliefs about large effects, can shed any light on the conflict between the two sets of results.

19.2 The data and a non-Bayesian analysis

In each of the first eight trials, two groups of patients with myocardial infarction were monitored. The patients in one group were administered magnesium intravenously; the patients in the other group, a control group, were administered a placebo.

A placebo is an inactive substance.

In the ith trial, let x_i^M denote the number of deaths from the n_i^M patients in the magnesium group. Similarly, let x_i^C denote the number of deaths from the n_i^C patients in the control group. Then x_i^M and x_i^C are independent observations on random variables X_i^M and X_i^C.

The data from the eight trials are in Table 19.1.

Table 19.1   Data from eight studies into the effect of magnesium on myocardial infarction

Trial number i	Magnesium group		Control group	
	Deaths x_i^M	Patients n_i^M	Deaths x_i^C	Patients n_i^C
1	1	40	2	36
2	9	135	23	135
3	2	200	7	200
4	1	48	1	46
5	10	150	8	148
6	1	59	9	56
7	1	25	3	23
8	90	1159	118	1157

Higgins, J.P.T. and Spiegelhalter, D.J. (2002) Being sceptical about meta-analyses: a Bayesian perspective on magnesium trials in myocardial infarction. *International Journal of Epidemiology*, **31**, 96–104.

A binomial model is assumed for the data: for $i = 1, 2, \ldots, 8$,

$$X_i^M \sim B(n_i^M, \theta_i^M), \quad X_i^C \sim B(n_i^C, \theta_i^C),$$

where θ_i^M and θ_i^C are unknown parameters; θ_i^M is the probability of death for a patient administered magnesium in trial i, and θ_i^C is the corresponding probability for a patient receiving a placebo.

Let OR_i denote the underlying odds ratio for trial i. The odds ratio OR_i is defined as

$$OR_i = \frac{\theta_i^M/(1 - \theta_i^M)}{\theta_i^C/(1 - \theta_i^C)}. \tag{19.1}$$

This is the ratio of the odds of death for patients administered magnesium to the odds of death for patients given a placebo.

The odds ratio is a standard measure of association in trials such as this. In this case, an odds ratio of 1 reflects no association between administered magnesium and death.

In a standard non-Bayesian analysis of the data in Table 19.1, each odds ratio OR_i is estimated by the sample odds ratio

$$\widehat{OR}_i = \frac{x_i^M(n_i^C - x_i^C)}{x_i^C(n_i^M - x_i^M)}.$$

Estimated odds ratios, together with approximate 95% confidence intervals (CIs), are shown in Table 19.2.

The estimated odds ratios are less than 1 for seven of the eight trials, indicating that magnesium has a protective effect. However, the value 1 is included in the approximate 95% confidence intervals for five of the eight trials. Some of the confidence intervals are very wide because the trials did not involve many patients. The results of the largest trial, trial 8, suggest a protective effect.

Of course, what is really of interest is some overall measure of the effect of magnesium, based on the data from all eight trials. Using a standard method which assumes that the sample odds ratios from the trials are all estimates of the same quantity OR, the overall odds ratio, a non-Bayesian estimate of OR is 0.64, with approximate 95% confidence interval $(0.50, 0.82)$.

The estimate of the overall odds ratio OR is small at 0.64, indicating that magnesium reduces the odds of mortality by 36%. Furthermore, the approximate 95% confidence interval does not contain the value 1. So pooling the information from the eight trials leads to a conclusion that there is strong evidence that magnesium has a protective effect on patients with myocardial infarction.

Table 19.2   Non-Bayesian analysis of the eight trials

i	$\widehat{OR}_i$	95% CI
1	0.436	$(0.038, 5.022)$
2	0.348	$(0.154, 0.783)$
3	0.278	$(0.057, 1.357)$
4	0.957	$(0.058, 15.773)$
5	1.250	$(0.479, 3.261)$
6	0.090	$(0.011, 0.736)$
7	0.278	$(0.027, 2.883)$
8	0.741	$(0.556, 0.988)$

In the mega-trial, there were 2216 deaths out of 29 011 patients in the magnesium group, and 2103 deaths out of 29 039 patients in the control group:

$$x^M = 2216, \quad n^M = 29\,011,$$
$$x^C = 2103, \quad n^C = 29\,039.$$

The estimated odds ratio is 1.059, with approximate 95% confidence interval $(0.996, 1.127)$. The estimate of the odds ratio is very close to 1, and the 95% confidence interval includes the value 1 and is very narrow. This suggests that magnesium has no effect on patients with myocardial infarction.

The results of the mega-trial conflict with those from the meta-analysis of the eight smaller trials.

19.3 Bayesian modelling and analysis

A Bayesian analysis of the data from the eight smaller trials that mimics the non-Bayesian analysis is possible. On its own, incorporating prior information in the form of the experts' beliefs about large effects is not enough to reconcile the discrepant results between the eight small trials and the mega-trial. Therefore a slightly more sophisticated Bayesian model will be adopted.

As in the non-Bayesian analysis, binomial models will be assumed for the numbers of deaths among patients receiving magnesium and patients receiving a placebo in the ith trial $(i = 1, 2, \ldots, 8)$:

$$X_i^M \sim B(n_i^M, \theta_i^M),$$
$$X_i^C \sim B(n_i^C, \theta_i^C),$$

where θ_i^M and θ_i^C are unknown parameters. The parameter θ_i^M represents the probability of death for a patient administered magnesium in trial i, and θ_i^C represents the corresponding probability for a patient receiving a placebo.

The odds ratio in trial i, OR_i, is defined as in Formula (19.1). The odds ratio cannot take negative values. However, the logarithm of the odds ratio, the **log odds ratio**, is unrestricted, so it is convenient to work with the log odds ratio. Let $\delta_i = \log(OR_i)$ be the log odds ratio for trial i, and let $\delta = \log(OR)$ be the overall log odds ratio. This overall log odds ratio is the quantity of primary interest in the analysis.

In the non-Bayesian analysis, it was assumed that the underlying odds ratio for each of the eight trials is equal to some overall odds ratio OR, that is, $OR_1 = OR_2 = \cdots = OR_8 = OR$. For the Bayesian analysis, a slightly different model will be assumed, in which

$$\delta_i \sim N(\delta, \sigma^2), \quad i = 1, 2, \ldots, 8.$$

This means that the δ_i have a normal distribution with mean equal to δ. This model allows the odds ratios in the trials to be different. The δ_i are called **random effects** because they have prior distributions and are not assumed to be fixed values. The model that was used for the non-Bayesian analysis, that assumed $\delta_i = \delta$ for $i = 1, 2, \ldots, 8$, is known as a **fixed-effects model**.

The distributional form of the prior distributions for the δ_i has been specified, but δ, the overall log odds ratio, and σ^2, the variance of the normal prior distribution, must also be specified. As this is a Bayesian analysis, prior distributions must be specified for all the unknown quantities in the model.

Prior distribution for δ

Since δ is the quantity of primary interest, it is this quantity that the experts have prior beliefs about. Some of the experts were sceptical about large effects. In fact, two experts stated that

> Most clinically important interventions are likely to reduce the relative risk of major outcomes, such as myocardial infarction, stroke, or death, by about 10–20%.

This was translated by the statisticians Higgins and Spiegelhalter into a probability of 0.05 that magnesium would reduce the odds of mortality by more than 25%. In this case study, Higgins and Spiegelhalter's interpretation of the experts' belief will be used.

First assume that δ has a normal prior distribution with mean a and variance b,

$$\delta \sim N(a, b).$$

It is usual to assume that δ is centred on 0, indicating no effect (that is, an odds ratio of 1). This corresponds to choosing $a = 0$. The experts' beliefs can be used to specify a value for the variance b.

A 25% reduction in the odds of mortality is equivalent to an odds ratio of 0.75, or a log odds ratio of $\log 0.75$, so Higgins and Spiegelhalter's interpretation of the experts' beliefs is equivalent to

$$P(\delta < \log 0.75) = 0.05.$$

Since

$$P(\delta < \log 0.75) = P\left(Z < \frac{\log 0.75 - 0}{\sqrt{b}}\right),$$

where $Z \sim N(0, 1)$, it follows that

$$\frac{\log 0.75}{\sqrt{b}} = -1.645.$$

If $\delta \sim N(0, b)$, then

$$Z = \frac{\delta - 0}{\sqrt{b}} \sim N(0, 1).$$

The 0.05-quantile of $N(0, 1)$ is -1.645.

Therefore

$$b = \left(\frac{\log 0.75}{-1.645}\right)^2 \simeq 0.0306.$$

So the prior distribution for the log odds ratio is

$$\delta \sim N(0, 0.0306).$$

Prior distribution for σ^2

A prior for the variance σ^2 of the prior distributions for the δ_i also needs to be specified. This is done by specifying a prior distribution for σ. Since there is little expert opinion on this value, a weak prior is chosen:

$$\sigma \sim U(0, 100).$$

Other prior distributions

Although prior distributions have been placed on each of the log odds ratios δ_i, this is not enough to complete the specification. Each log odds ratio is actually a function of two quantities: θ_i^M and θ_i^C. Therefore, to complete the model, a prior needs to be specified for each θ_i^C; the prior distribution for θ_i^M is determined by the prior distributions for θ_i^C and δ_i.

Although the experts have prior opinions about the odds ratio, they have little opinion about the probability of death in the control group: it could take any value between 0 and 1, and no value is more likely than any other. Therefore the natural choice of prior is the uniform distribution on $(0, 1)$, that is,

$$\theta_i^C \sim U(0, 1).$$

The full Bayesian model

All the unknown quantities in the model have been assigned prior distributions. The full Bayesian model is as follows: for $i = 1, 2, \ldots, 8$,

$$X_i^{\mathrm{M}} \sim B(n_i^{\mathrm{M}}, \theta_i^{\mathrm{M}}),$$
$$X_i^{\mathrm{C}} \sim B(n_i^{\mathrm{C}}, \theta_i^{\mathrm{C}}),$$
$$\theta_i^{\mathrm{C}} \sim U(0, 1),$$
$$\delta_i \sim N(\delta, \sigma^2),$$
$$\delta \sim N(0, 0.0306),$$
$$\sigma \sim U(0, 100).$$

This is known as a **hierarchical model** because of its hierarchical structure. It is also known as a **random-effects model** because the log odds ratio is allowed to vary randomly between studies.

This is quite a complicated model. MCMC is ideally suited for making inferences about the unknown quantities.

Weak prior beliefs

The model just described incorporates a prior distribution for the log odds ratio which attempts to capture the sceptical beliefs of some experts. It is also interesting to compare the analysis of this model with that from a Bayesian analysis that does not incorporate expert opinion and attempts to mimic a non-Bayesian analysis. This might highlight the benefit of incorporating expert opinion when it is available, and would provide a further comparison between the Bayesian and non-Bayesian analyses.

In order to mimic a non-Bayesian analysis, the prior distribution for δ would be a normal distribution, centred at 0, but with very large variance: $\delta \sim N(0, 1000)$.

Bayesian analysis of the mega-trial

The Bayesian model for the analysis of the mega-trial is as follows:

$$X^{\mathrm{M}} \sim B(n^{\mathrm{M}}, \theta^{\mathrm{M}}),$$
$$X^{\mathrm{C}} \sim B(n^{\mathrm{C}}, \theta^{\mathrm{C}}),$$
$$\theta^{\mathrm{C}} \sim U(0, 1),$$
$$\delta \sim N(0, 0.0306),$$

where δ is the overall log odds ratio.

Although this is a much simpler model than the one for the eight small trials, MCMC is still the best way to sample from the posterior distribution for the parameters.

Three sequences of 10 000 values with initial values sampled from the prior distribution were simulated. Using trace plots of simulated values, a burn-in of 1000 iterations was chosen. Based on a final sample of 27 000 values from the posterior distribution, an estimate of the posterior mean of the overall odds ratio OR is 1.057 (0.0004). An estimate of the equal-tailed 95% credible interval for the odds ratio is $(0.995, 1.123)$.

Since the mega-trial contains such a large amount of data, even with the sceptical prior for δ, the results from the Bayesian analysis of the mega-trial are similar to those from the non-Bayesian analysis reported in Subsection 19.2.

19.4   Practical implementation

In this subsection, you will use WinBUGS to carry out a Bayesian analysis of the data on magnesium and myocardial infarction from the first eight trials.

Refer to Chapter 13 of Computer Book 4 for the work in this subsection.

19.5   Conclusions and further analyses

The main conclusion from this case study is that if prior information is available, then it makes sense to incorporate it into a Bayesian analysis. In the case of the meta-analysis, the results from the first eight trials did not look so good after combining them with the expert scepticism. Perhaps if a Bayesian random-effects analysis using this sceptical prior had been carried out in 1993, the mega-trial might not have gone ahead, and vast amounts of money might have been saved.

In addition to the choice of prior, the case study also highlights the importance of the choice of model itself. The choice of a random-effects model turned out to be very important. It is beyond the scope of a course such as this to delve into the finer details of statistical modelling, but nevertheless you should have gained some idea of the scope and flexibility that the Bayesian approach to statistics brings to this problem. Essentially, with the use of MCMC, you are free to explore a wide range of realistic, but possibly very complicated, models for the data under study. WinBUGS is a valuable tool in facilitating this exploration.

Summary of Section 19

In this section, a case study involving the Bayesian analysis of data from studies into the effect of magnesium on patients with myocardial infarction has been described. You have seen that incorporating prior information into a Bayesian analysis can be very important. The model for the data involved many unknown parameters. MCMC was used to sample from the posterior distribution of the parameters in the model. You have seen the ease with which such a complicated model is handled by WinBUGS.

20 Exercises on Book 4

Exercise 20.1   Screening for breast cancer

Breast screening is a method of detecting breast cancer at a very early stage. The first step involves taking an X-ray of each breast called a mammogram. The mammogram can reveal small changes in breast tissue which may indicate the presence of cancers that are too small to be felt. However, a mammogram is not perfect, and cancer may not be detected, or the mammogram may detect an abnormality which is in fact not cancer.

In a breast cancer screening programme, an initial mammogram would detect 87% of undiagnosed cancers of the breast in women aged between 40 and 49, and would falsely detect cancers in about 5% of women in this age group who do not have cancer. Breast cancer is not very common in women aged between 40 and 49, and only approximately 0.1% of women screened in this age range will have cancer. Suppose that two women, Emma and Helen, are both aged between 40 and 49, and are due to go for an initial mammogram.

Kerlikowske, K., Grady, D., Barclay, J., Sickles, E.A. and Ernster, V. (1996) Effect of age, breast density, and family history on the sensitivity of first screening mammography. *Journal of the American Medical Association*, **276**, no. 1, 33–38.

(a) What is the estimated prior probability that Emma has breast cancer? What is the estimated prior probability that Helen has breast cancer?

(b) Emma's mammogram detects an abnormality which may be cancer. What is the posterior probability that Emma has breast cancer?

(c) Helen's mammogram does not detect any abnormality. What is the posterior probability that Helen has breast cancer?

Exercise 20.2   Posterior for Slater School

In Example 3.1, the parameter θ was the probability of developing cancer (the cancer rate) at Slater School. There were four possible values: 0.03, 0.04, 0.05 and 0.06. The prior for θ has the probability mass function shown in Table 20.1.

Table 20.1   A prior distribution for θ

θ	0.03	0.04	0.05	0.06
$p(\theta)$	$\frac{1}{2}$	$\frac{1}{6}$	$\frac{1}{6}$	$\frac{1}{6}$

The random variable X represents the number of staff at Slater School who developed cancer. The likelihood of θ after observing that 8 of the 145 staff at the school had developed cancer is given in Table 20.2.

See Activity 3.7.

Table 20.2   The likelihood of θ

θ	0.03	0.04	0.05	0.06
$L(\theta)$	0.040	0.097	0.138	0.139

(a) A generalization of Formula (2.4) leads to

$$P(X = 8) = P(X = 8|\theta = 0.03)P(\theta = 0.03)$$
$$+ P(X = 8|\theta = 0.04)P(\theta = 0.04)$$
$$+ P(X = 8|\theta = 0.05)P(\theta = 0.05)$$
$$+ P(X = 8|\theta = 0.06)P(\theta = 0.06).$$

Use this result to show that $P(X = 8) \simeq 0.0823$.

(b) Use Formula (2.3) to calculate the posterior distribution for θ.

(c) Comment on how observing $X = 8$ has affected your prior beliefs. What is the most likely value of θ, given that $X = 8$?

(d) Calculate the posterior probability that the cancer rate is higher at Slater school than nationally (where it is 0.03).

Exercise 20.3   *Models for standard priors*

Show that the two priors in each of the following pairs have the same mode.

(a) Beta(6, 4) and Beta(31, 19)

(b) Gamma(11, 2) and Gamma(1.5, 0.1)

(c) $N(10, 0.2)$ and $N(10, 100.2)$

Exercise 20.4   *Strengths of standard priors*

For each of the following pairs, identify the prior which is the stronger.

(a) Beta(4, 4) and Beta(40, 40)

(b) Beta(5, 12) and Beta(12, 5)

(c) $N(4, 10)$ and $N(10, 4)$

Exercise 20.5   *Paediatric cardiology*

In Activities 5.9 and 8.2, the problem of diagnosing a heart problem in a baby, given information provided over the telephone, was considered. One aspect in diagnosing heart problems concerns measuring oxygen pressure (pO_2). In this exercise, the parameter ϕ of interest is defined as follows:

$$\phi = P(\text{baby with transposition of the great arteries has } pO_2 < 3.5).$$

The symbol ϕ is a Greek letter pronounced 'fye'.

Three consultant paediatric cardiologists were asked their opinion about ϕ. A Beta(42.5, 7.5) distribution was used to represent their prior beliefs about ϕ. Of 50 babies observed with transposition of the great arteries, 23 were observed to have a value of pO_2 less than 3.5.

(a) Explain why a beta prior is the natural standard prior to use for ϕ.

(b) Calculate the prior mode and prior standard deviation for ϕ.

(c) Calculate the posterior distribution for ϕ, given the data.

(d) Calculate the posterior mode and standard deviation for ϕ.

(e) A plot of the prior, likelihood and posterior for ϕ is shown in Figure 20.1.

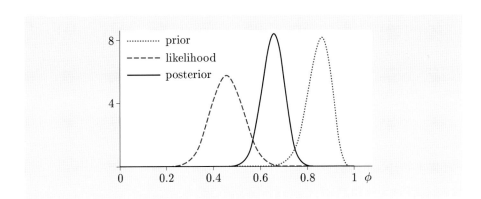

Figure 20.1   Prior, likelihood and posterior for ϕ

Use this plot, together with your answers to parts (b) and (d), to discuss how the data have affected the prior beliefs about ϕ.

Exercise 20.6   Alzheimer's progression: an alternative opinion

In Example 8.4, the natural progression of Alzheimer's disease was considered. The parameter of interest is θ, the mean change in the value of an index measuring aspects of short-term memory, one year after the diagnosis of Alzheimer's disease. The changes in the index are assumed to be normally distributed, $N(\theta, 100)$.

Suppose that a second researcher involved in the study believed that the most likely value for θ is -30, and that her assessed values for the quartiles of the prior for μ are $L = -33$ and $U = -25$.

(a) Calculate the values of the parameters of the normal prior $N(a, b)$ which matches the researcher's assessed values approximately.

(b) The sample mean for the change in index values for 20 Alzheimer's patients is -36. Calculate the posterior for θ.

(c) Calculate the 95% HPD interval for θ.

Exercise 20.7   Another model for the albacore tuna data

In Example 17.1, a normal model with unknown mean and variance was proposed for data on the annual catch of albacore tuna. In this exercise, the following weak priors will be used for the mean μ and the precision $\tau = \sigma^{-2}$:

$$\mu \sim \text{Gamma}(1, 0.1),$$
$$\tau \sim \text{Gamma}(1, 0.1).$$

Values are simulated from the joint posterior distribution for μ and τ using MCMC.

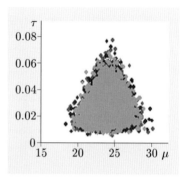

(a) Figure 20.2 shows a scatterplot of values simulated from the joint posterior distribution for μ and τ.

Use the scatterplot to comment briefly on the relationship between μ and τ. Are the posterior distributions for μ and τ independent?

Figure 20.2   Scatterplot of values from the joint posterior distribution for μ and τ

(b) In the simulation, $N = 10\,000$ values were obtained from the joint posterior distribution for μ and τ. (You may assume that values from the burn-in period were discarded.)

The posterior means of μ and τ, the posterior standard deviations and the MC errors are given in Table 20.3.

The MC errors were calculated allowing for dependence between successive simulated values.

Table 20.3   Posterior means, standard deviations and MC errors

Parameter	Posterior mean	Posterior SD	MC error
μ	24.1	1.301	0.0147
τ	0.0284	0.008 25	0.000 083 9

(i)   Is the sample size N adequate? Justify your answer.

(ii) Comment briefly on the relative contribution of the data and the priors in determining the posterior means and standard deviations of μ and τ. Suggest a reason for your finding.

Summary of Book 4

Part I

A central tenet of the Bayesian approach to statistics is that all knowledge of unknown quantities can be expressed in terms of probabilities. These probabilities can sometimes be calculated exactly, or estimated using observed or hypothesized relative frequencies. However, more subjective methods are often required. Probabilities can be combined using Bayes' theorem, which provides a way of updating an initial probability estimate in the light of new evidence. In the Bayesian approach to inference about a parameter θ, uncertainty about its value is represented by a probability distribution. Bayesian inference is based on the interplay between the prior distribution for θ, the likelihood of θ for data collected about θ, and the posterior distribution for θ, given the data. The prior distribution summarizes prior beliefs about the true value of θ. The likelihood function summarizes the information about θ, conditional on the data that have been observed: the larger the value of the likelihood is, the more likely is the corresponding value of θ. The posterior distribution for θ, given the data, combines the prior distribution and the likelihood, and is obtained, up to a constant of proportionality, by multiplying together the prior distribution and the likelihood. The posterior distribution summarizes all the available information about θ.

Part II

Four families of standard distributions that are commonly used as priors are the normal, uniform, beta and gamma families. When specifying a prior, assessments of its location and spread are required. The location is assessed most easily using the mode or the median. The spread can be assessed using appropriate quantiles: specifying either the central 50% or the central two-thirds of the prior is recommended. The prior parameters can be calculated from the assessments of the location and spread — by hand for the normal prior, or using a computer for the beta and gamma priors. A conjugate analysis is one in which the posterior is of the same distributional form as the prior. Conjugate analyses are mathematically simple and allow the prior and posterior to be compared easily. However, a conjugate analysis is not always possible or appropriate. The posterior contains all the current information regarding θ. It is always a good idea to obtain a plot of the posterior. The posterior distribution should also be summarized using the mode, mean or median and the variance or quantiles. Credible intervals give a range of values within which most of the posterior distribution lies, and thus provide posterior interval estimates of θ. Either highest posterior density or equal-tailed credible intervals may be used.

Part III

Stochastic simulation can be used to sample values from standard probability distributions. It can also be used to make inferences about a Bayesian posterior distribution that is too difficult to derive mathematically. The simulated values are analysed using graphical and numerical summaries. An appropriate graphical summary is a density histogram. Appropriate numerical summaries include the mean and the median for measures of location, and the variance and the standard deviation for measures of dispersion. Any quantity of interest can be estimated by its equivalent based on the sample of values. An example of this is the equal-tailed $100(1 - \alpha)\%$ credible interval, which gives a measure of posterior spread. As with samples of data, some appreciation of the sampling variability from a stochastic simulation is needed. For values sampled independently from a particular probability distribution, the sampling variability decreases as the sample size increases. The Monte Carlo standard error is a measure of the accuracy of a sample mean estimate.

Simulation allows functions of parameters to be dealt with easily. The more unknown parameters there are in the Bayesian model, the more useful simulation becomes. An example of a model with more than one unknown parameter is the normal model with unknown mean and variance. A normal-gamma distribution is a conjugate prior distribution for this model. An important aspect of simulation from a joint distribution of two parameters is that a sample from the marginal distribution of a parameter is obtained by taking the sampled values of that parameter.

Part IV

Markov chain Monte Carlo is a powerful method that allows inferences to be made about the parameters in a Bayesian model. Sampled values from a Markov chain settle down to an equilibrium distribution, and successive values are dependent. These two factors need to be accounted for before inferences based on the sampled values can be made. It is good practice to monitor the simulated values from a small number of chains, with initial values sampled from the prior distribution. A trace plot of these sampled values can be useful for assessing convergence. The dependence of successive values affects the Monte Carlo standard error.

When a Bayesian model involves more than one unknown parameter, it is often easier to specify independent marginal prior distributions for the parameters than to specify a multivariate joint prior distribution. Doing so often leads to a non-conjugate analysis which can be carried out easily using MCMC. Another situation which often requires MCMC is when a prior distribution is specified for a transformation of a parameter.

Learning outcomes

You have been working to acquire the following skills.

Part I

◇   Use relative frequencies to estimate probabilities.

◇   Calculate posterior probabilities using Bayes' theorem.

◇   Describe the role of the prior distribution, the likelihood function and the posterior distribution in Bayesian inference about a parameter θ.

◇   Interpret the prior distribution for θ.

◇   Interpret the likelihood function for θ.

◇   Describe how the prior distribution and the likelihood function are combined to obtain the posterior distribution.

◇   Interpret the posterior distribution for θ, given the data.

◇   Use *LearnBayes* to explore prior to posterior analyses for a proportion.

Part II

◇ Select an appropriate standard prior distribution for a parameter θ.

◇ Interpret standard prior distributions, and explain how they may be used to represent differing strengths of beliefs.

◇ Describe noninformative priors and improper uniform priors.

◇ Assess the location of a prior using the mode or median.

◇ Assess the spread of a prior using equal-tailed intervals.

◇ Calculate the parameters of a normal prior using the assessed location and spread.

◇ Explain what is meant by a conjugate analysis.

◇ Describe prior to posterior analyses for the beta/binomial, gamma/Poisson and normal/normal models.

◇ Describe prior to posterior analyses for the uniform/binomial, uniform/Poisson and uniform/normal models.

◇ Summarize and interpret the posterior location using the mode in conjugate analyses.

◇ Summarize and interpret the posterior spread using the variance or standard deviation in conjugate analyses.

◇ Interpret credible intervals for a parameter θ.

◇ Explain what is meant by HPD and equal-tailed credible intervals.

◇ Calculate credible intervals for a normal posterior.

◇ Calculate posterior probabilities for a normal posterior.

◇ Use *LearnBayes* to explore conjugate prior to posterior analyses.

◇ Use *LearnBayes* to obtain posterior summaries for conjugate analyses.

Part III

◇ Choose an appropriate graphical method to display sampled values from a probability distribution.

◇ Interpret graphical summaries of simulated values.

◇ Appreciate the effect of sample size on sampling variability.

◇ Derive an estimate of the equal-tailed $100(1 - \alpha)\%$ credible interval for an unknown quantity, based on appropriate sample quantiles, and interpret this interval.

◇ Manipulate simulated values of a parameter (or parameters) so that they represent simulated values of a transformation of that parameter (or parameters).

◇ Interpret a scatterplot of values from a bivariate probability distribution.

◇ Manipulate simulated values from a joint distribution to obtain simulated values from one of its marginal distributions.

◇ Use WinBUGS to simulate values from a standard probability distribution, and analyse the sampled values.

◇ Use WinBUGS to simulate values from joint distributions and marginal distributions, or from the distribution of a function of one or more parameters.

Part IV

◇   Describe the main steps involved in the standard procedure for dealing with
MCMC samples.

◇   Choose appropriate initial values for an MCMC simulation.

◇   Assess convergence from trace plots.

◇   Determine an appropriate burn-in period based on inspection of trace plots.

◇   Interpret graphical and numerical summaries of sampled values from MCMC
simulations.

◇   Use WinBUGS to run MCMC simulations, and to obtain graphical and
numerical summaries of sampled values.

Solutions to Activities

Solution 1.1

P(even number)

$= \dfrac{\text{number of faces on the die with even numbers}}{\text{number of faces on the die}}$

$= \dfrac{3}{6} = \dfrac{1}{2}.$

Solution 1.2

(a) Relative frequencies calculated from the data can be used to estimate these probabilities.

(i) The probability that a man dies of CHD can be estimated as

$\dfrac{\text{number of male deaths from CHD}}{\text{number of male deaths}} = \dfrac{64\,473}{288\,332}$

$\simeq 0.2236.$

(ii) The probability that a woman dies of CHD can be estimated as

$\dfrac{\text{number of female deaths from CHD}}{\text{number of female deaths}} = \dfrac{53\,003}{318\,463}$

$\simeq 0.1664.$

(b) These estimates are based on large amounts of data from 2002. Assuming that the probability of death from CHD has not changed since 2002, these estimates will be very good. Of course, it is possible that the probability of death from CHD may change over time, so it is important to bear in mind that the further in the future the year is, the less reliable these estimates may be.

Solution 1.3

It is easier to recall words which begin with r (*r*un, *r*abbits, ...) than words with r as the third letter (pa*r*k, bi*r*d, ...). Consequently, most people judge it more likely that an English word begins with r than that r is the third letter, that is, $p_1 > p_3$. In fact, the reverse is true: $p_3 > p_1$. This is an example of possible probability estimation bias, where the person making the estimate links the probability to the frequency with which they can recall occurrences, rather than the frequency with which the event actually occurs.

(Adapted from: Tversky, A. and Kahneman, D. (1973) Availability: a heuristic for judging frequency and probability. *Cognitive Psychology*, **5**, 207–232.)

Solution 2.1

(a) (i) From Table 2.2,

P(Down's|mother's age $= 25$ years) $= 1/1352$

(ii) From Table 2.2,

P(Down's|mother's age $= 40$ years) $= 1/97.$

(b) To compare the numbers of pregnancies affected by Down's syndrome, the total numbers of pregnancies in women aged 25 and in women aged 40 are required. This information is not available, so it is not possible to conclude that more foetuses with Down's syndrome occur in pregnant women aged 40 than in pregnant women aged 25.

Solution 2.2

(a) Using the data in Table 2.1 gives the estimate

$P(X = \text{male}|Y = \text{yes})$

$= \dfrac{\text{number of male deaths from CHD}}{\text{total number of deaths from CHD}}$

$= \dfrac{64\,473}{117\,476} \simeq 0.5488.$

(b) Using Formula (2.1) gives

$P(X = \text{male}|Y = \text{yes})$

$= \dfrac{P(Y = \text{yes and } X = \text{male})}{P(Y = \text{yes})}$

$\simeq \dfrac{0.1063}{0.1936} \simeq 0.5491.$

This is the same to three decimal places as the estimate produced using the data in Table 2.1 directly. (The slight discrepancy is due to rounding error.)

Solution 2.3

(a) From Table 2.1, an estimate of the conditional probability is given by

$P(Y = \text{yes}|X = \text{female}) = \dfrac{53\,003}{318\,463} \simeq 0.1664.$

(b) Using Formula (2.4),

$P(Y = \text{yes})$

$= P(Y = \text{yes}|X = \text{male}) \times P(X = \text{male})$

$\quad + P(Y = \text{yes}|X = \text{female}) \times P(X = \text{female}).$

Since $P(X = \text{male}) + P(X = \text{female}) = 1$,

$P(X = \text{female}) = 1 - P(X = \text{male})$

$\simeq 1 - 0.4752$

$= 0.5248.$

Hence an estimate of $P(Y = \text{yes})$ is given by

$P(Y = \text{yes}) \simeq 0.2236 \times 0.4752 + 0.1664 \times 0.5248$

$\simeq 0.1936.$

This is the same as the estimate found directly from the contingency table in Example 2.1.

Solution 2.4

In Example 2.6, you saw that
$$P(\text{Adams guilty}|M) \simeq \frac{1 \times \frac{1}{200\,000}}{P(M)},$$
where $P(M)$ is given by

$P(M|\text{Adams guilty}) \times P(\text{Adams guilty})$
$\quad + P(M|\text{Adams not guilty}) \times P(\text{Adams not guilty}).$

Using the prosecution's estimate of $\frac{1}{200\,000\,000}$ for
$P(M|\text{Adams not guilty})$ gives

$$P(M) \simeq 1 \times \frac{1}{200\,000} + \frac{1}{200\,000\,000} \times \left(1 - \frac{1}{200\,000}\right)$$
$$= \frac{200\,000\,000}{200\,000\,000 \times 200\,000} + \frac{199\,999}{200\,000\,000 \times 200\,000}$$
$$= \frac{200\,199\,999}{200\,000\,000 \times 200\,000}.$$

Thus

$P(\text{Adams guilty}|M)$

$$\simeq \left(1 \times \frac{1}{200\,000}\right) \Big/ \frac{200\,199\,999}{200\,000\,000 \times 200\,000}$$
$$= \frac{200\,000\,000}{200\,199\,999}$$
$$\simeq 0.999.$$

Since the probability is very close to 1, this could well be evidence of guilt 'beyond all reasonable doubt'. Thus, based on the prosecution's estimate of $P(M|\text{Adams not guilty})$ and the prosecution's evidence M, the judge and jury may well believe Adams to be guilty. However, evidence from the defence has not yet been considered.

Solution 2.5

In the solution to Activity 2.4, you calculated $P(\text{Adams guilty}|M)$ to be 0.999 using the prosecution's estimate of $P(M|\text{Adams not guilty})$. This probability can be updated after observing E_1 and E_2, using the method of Example 2.7, but with $P(\text{Adams guilty}|M) = 0.999$.

First, updating for E_1, (2.10) gives
$$P(E_1|M) \simeq 0.1 \times 0.999 + 0.9 \times (1 - 0.999)$$
$$= 0.1008.$$

Then (2.9) leads to
$$P(\text{Adams guilty}|E_1, M) = \frac{0.1 \times 0.999}{0.1008} \simeq 0.991.$$

Secondly, updating for E_2, (2.12) becomes
$$P(E_2|E_1, M) \simeq 0.25 \times 0.991 + 0.5 \times (1 - 0.991)$$
$$= 0.252\,25.$$

Using this value in (2.11) leads to
$$P(\text{Adams guilty}|E_2, E_1, M) \simeq \frac{0.25 \times 0.991}{0.252\,25} \simeq 0.98.$$

With the prosecution's estimate of $P(M|\text{Adams not guilty}) = 1/200\,000\,000$, the posterior probability of guilt after all the evidence (M, E_1, E_2) has been considered is very close to 1. This may well be judged evidence of guilt 'beyond all reasonable doubt'.

Solution 3.1

The prior beliefs about θ are expressed through the prior distribution. From the prior distribution, the value $\theta = 0.03$ has the largest probability, so the value 0.03 is the most likely value of θ.

Solution 3.2

(a) A sketch of a possible prior density is shown in Figure S.1.

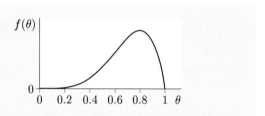

Figure S.1   A possible prior density for θ

Notice that the density has a peak at $\theta = 0.8$, as 0.8 is believed to be the most likely value for θ. Also, the density lies between the values 0.1 and 1 to reflect the belief that θ is unlikely to be smaller than 0.1. Since 0.8, the most likely value for θ, is not equidistant between 0.1 and 1, this density is skewed.

(b) A sketch of a possible prior density is shown in Figure S.2.

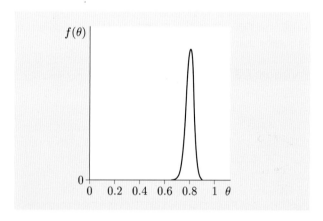

Figure S.2   A possible prior density for θ

Both this prior density and the one for part (a) have a peak at $\theta = 0.8$, as 0.8 is believed to be the most likely value for θ in each case. However, the prior density in Figure S.2 is narrower and taller than the prior density in Figure S.1 because the range of likely values for θ is smaller for the prior density in Figure S.2, but the area under the curve is 1 for both densities. Both densities are skewed.

(c) A sketch of a possible prior density is shown in Figure S.3.

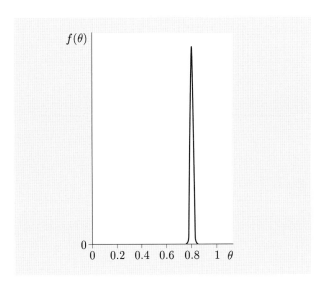

Figure S.3 A possible prior density for θ

Notice that the entire density is concentrated around the value 0.8 because you are almost certain that θ is 0.8.

(d) The sketch of the prior density is shown in Figure S.4.

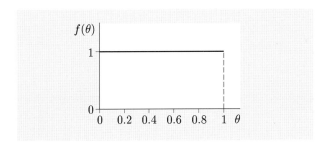

Figure S.4 The prior density for θ

Notice that all possible values of θ between 0 and 1 are equally likely: the density is flat. You might use a prior density like this if you have no idea what the value of θ is.

(e) The prior density in Figure S.4 is the weakest as it represents the fact that no information is available about θ. The prior density in Figure S.1 is also fairly weak, as the range of likely values includes almost all values between 0 and 1. The prior density in Figure S.2 is stronger, representing greater confidence that θ lies in a narrower range of values. The prior density in Figure S.3 is the strongest prior density, as this represents virtual certainty that 0.8 is the value of θ. In reality, it is unlikely that such a strong prior density would represent your belief about θ.

Solution 3.3

(a) Since X can take only two values, male and female,

$$P(X = \text{female}|Y = \text{yes})$$
$$= 1 - P(X = \text{male}|Y = \text{yes})$$
$$\simeq 1 - 0.5488 = 0.4512.$$

The probabilities $P(X = \text{male}|Y = \text{yes})$ and $P(X = \text{female}|Y = \text{yes})$ give the conditional distribution of X, given $Y = \text{yes}$.

(b) Since $P(X = \text{male}) \simeq 0.4752$, it follows that $P(X = \text{female}) \simeq 0.5248$. Thus the distribution of X is indeed different from the conditional distribution of X, given $Y = \text{yes}$.

Solution 3.4

(a) A value of X less than 0 is more likely in a foetus without Down's syndrome: the value 0 is close to the median of $f(x|\text{not Down's})$, but well below the median of $f(x|\text{Down's})$.

(b) A value of X greater than 2 is more likely in a foetus with Down's syndrome. The value of X is greater than 2 in very few foetuses without Down's syndrome, whereas such values are quite common in foetuses with Down's syndrome.

Solution 3.5

When $\theta = 0.2$, the p.m.f. of X is

$$P(X = x|\theta = 0.2) = \binom{50}{x} 0.2^x 0.8^{50-x}.$$

Solution 3.6

If $X = 14$, then the value 0.3 is more likely for θ than 0.2, because

$$P(X = 14|\theta = 0.3) > P(X = 14|\theta = 0.2).$$

Solution 3.7

(a) As the probability of developing cancer at Slater School is assumed to be the same for all 145 staff, and staff are assumed to develop cancer independently, X can be modelled by the binomial distribution $B(145, \theta)$. The parameter θ can take only four possible values: 0.03, 0.04, 0.05 or 0.06. Thus there are just four possible models: the binomial models $B(145, 0.03)$, $B(145, 0.04)$, $B(145, 0.05)$ and $B(145, 0.06)$.

The p.m.f. corresponding to the $B(145, 0.03)$ model is

$$P(X = x|\theta = 0.03) = \binom{145}{x} 0.03^x 0.97^{145-x}.$$

(b) The largest probability of observing $X = 8$ is when $\theta = 0.06$, so this is the most likely value of θ. Similarly, the least likely value of θ is 0.03.

Solution 5.1

(a) The most likely value of θ is the mode. For the prior in Figure 5.2(a), this is 15 000 km. For the prior in Figure 5.2(b), it is 12 000 km.

(b) In theory, all distances from $-\infty$ to ∞ are possible. However, in practice, only those corresponding to the 'bulges' in the densities are likely. For the prior in Figure 5.2(a), this likely range is about 13 500 to 16 500 km; for the prior in Figure 5.2(b), it is about 6000 to 18 000 km.

(c) The density in Figure 5.2(b) is more spread out, so the variance b is larger for this prior. The larger value of b represents greater prior uncertainty about θ.

Solution 5.2

The density for a $U(a, b)$ prior for θ is
$f(\theta) = 1/(b - a)$, for θ in the interval $[a, b]$.

(a) For $U(-10, 10)$,
$$f(\theta) = \tfrac{1}{20}, \quad -10 \le \theta \le 10.$$

(b) For $U(1.5, 6.2)$,
$$f(\theta) = \tfrac{1}{4.7}, \quad 1.5 \le \theta \le 6.2.$$
The densities are shown in Figure S.5.

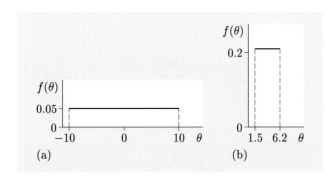

Figure S.5 Uniform densities: (a) $U(-10, 10)$ (b) $U(1.5, 6.2)$

Solution 5.3

The neuropsychologist's opinions can be represented by the uniform prior $U(-20, 30)$. The probability density function for this prior is
$$f(\theta) = \tfrac{1}{50}, \quad -20 \le \theta \le 30.$$

Solution 5.4

Using Formula (5.2), the Beta$(1, 1)$ distribution has density
$$f(\theta) = c\,\theta^{1-1}(1 - \theta)^{1-1}, \quad 0 \le \theta \le 1,$$
that is,
$$f(\theta) = c, \quad 0 \le \theta \le 1,$$
where c is the constant which ensures that the area under $f(\theta)$ is 1. Since $f(\theta)$ is constant, it is the density of a uniform distribution. In this case, c must be 1, since $f(\theta) = c$ only for values of θ between 0 and 1. However, from (5.1), the density for the uniform distribution $U(0, 1)$ is
$$f(\theta) = 1, \quad 0 \le \theta \le 1.$$

Thus the Beta$(1, 1)$ distribution is the $U(0, 1)$ distribution. Its density is shown in Figure S.6.

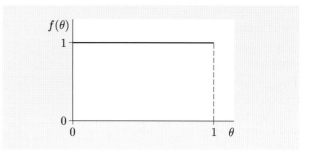

Figure S.6 The Beta$(1, 1)$ density

Solution 5.5

(a) Setting $a = b$ in Formula (5.3) gives
$$\text{mode} = \frac{b - 1}{b + b - 2} = \frac{b - 1}{2(b - 1)} = \frac{1}{2} = 0.5,$$
as required.

(b) (i) For the Beta$(5, 10)$ prior,
$$\text{mode} = \frac{5 - 1}{5 + 10 - 2} = \frac{4}{13}.$$

(ii) For the Beta$(10, 5)$ prior,
$$\text{mode} = \frac{10 - 1}{10 + 5 - 2} = \frac{9}{13}.$$
Hence
$$\text{mode of Beta}(5, 10) = 1 - \text{mode of Beta}(10, 5).$$

Solution 5.6

Using Formula (5.3), the mode of each of the three priors is 0.25. The values of $a + b$ for Beta$(2, 4)$, Beta$(16, 46)$ and Beta$(26, 76)$ are 6, 62 and 102, respectively. Hence Beta$(2, 4)$ represents the weakest prior beliefs (and hence is the least peaked), while Beta$(26, 76)$ represents the strongest prior beliefs (and hence is the most peaked of the three). The priors are shown in Figure S.7.

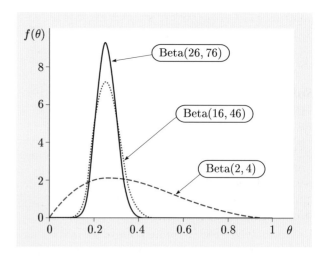

Figure S.7 Three beta priors

Solution 5.7

The mode of Gamma(a, b) is given by Formula (5.5): mode $= (a - 1)/b$.

For Gamma$(4, 0.1)$, mode $= (4 - 1)/0.1 = 30$.

For Gamma$(31, 1)$, mode $= (31 - 1)/1 = 30$.

Hence Gamma$(4, 0.1)$ and Gamma$(31, 1)$ have the same mode.

Two gamma priors have the same shape if the parameter a is the same for both. Therefore Gamma$(4, 1)$ and Gamma$(4, 0.1)$ have the same shape, and Gamma$(31, 1)$ and Gamma$(31, 0.1)$ have the same shape.

Solution 5.8

Since θ_{phone} can take only positive values, a gamma prior may be suitable. An improper uniform prior such as $U(0, \infty)$ might also be suitable.

Since θ_{junk} is a probability, a beta prior may be suitable. A uniform prior $U(a, b)$ may also be suitable (where $0 \leq a < b \leq 1$).

Solution 5.9

Since θ is a probability, it takes values between 0 and 1. Hence the beta prior is appropriate. The uniform prior $U(a, b)$ with $0 \leq a < b \leq 1$ could also be used.

Solution 5.10

Since θ can take both negative and positive values, a normal prior may be suitable. An improper uniform prior $U(-\infty, \infty)$ may also be suitable.

Solution 5.11

Since θ can take only positive values, a gamma prior may be suitable. If θ is expected to take only large values, then a normal prior might be adequate. An improper uniform prior $U(0, \infty)$ may also be suitable.

Solution 6.1

I believe that the most likely value for θ, the proportion of adults in Great Britain who trust politicians to tell the truth, is about one third, or 0.33. So my assessment of the mode of my prior distribution for θ is 0.33. You may well have different opinions about θ, and hence a different mode.

Solution 6.2

The modes for your priors are the values *you* believe are most likely for θ_{phone} and θ_{junk}. Here are *my* values.

I usually communicate by email and receive very few phone calls, so I estimate my mode for θ_{phone} to be quite low, 3 (say). Of course, the mode for your prior is likely to be different.

Unfortunately, I receive quite a lot of junk mail: on about one day out of three, I receive two or more items. So I estimate my mode for θ_{junk} to be 0.33. Again, the mode for your prior will probably be different.

Solution 6.4

The width of Lucy's interval is $275 - 185 = 90$. The width of Andrew's interval is $260 - 220 = 40$. Therefore Lucy's interval is wider than Andrew's. Hence Lucy's prior has greater spread than Andrew's, indicating that she is less confident about the distance than Andrew.

Solution 6.5

The interval $(0.55, 1.39)$ contains the middle 66% of the prior. Since the interval is equal-tailed, about 17% of the prior lies below 0.55, and 17% lies above 1.39 (and hence 83% lies below 1.39). Therefore 0.55 is the assessed value of $q_{0.17}$, and 1.39 is the assessed value of $q_{0.83}$.

Solution 6.6

The interval from the lower quartile of $f(\theta)$ $(q_{0.25})$ to the upper quartile $(q_{0.75})$ will contain the middle half of the prior.

In the solution to Activity 6.2, I assessed the mode for my prior for θ_{phone}, the mean number of telephone calls I receive each week, to be 3. My assessment of the interval containing the middle 50% of my prior for θ_{phone} is $(2, 5)$, so $q_{0.25} = 2$ and $q_{0.75} = 5$. Notice that I believe that the mode for $f(\theta)$ should be within the interval, but that the interval is not symmetric about the mode. Hence my prior is right-skew. This reflects the fact that while I believe that my value for θ_{phone} is likely to be close to 3, I do not wish to rule out values as large as 6. It is important to remember that the assessed quartiles for your prior may be very different from mine!

In Activity 6.2, I assessed the mode for my prior for θ_{junk} to be 0.33. My assessment of the interval containing the middle 50% of my prior for θ_{junk} is $(0.25, 0.55)$, so $q_{0.25} = 0.25$ and $q_{0.75} = 0.55$. Notice that I believe that the mode for $f(\theta)$ should be within the interval, and that the interval is not symmetric about the mode. Again remember that your quartiles may be very different from mine!

Solution 6.8

The assessed median is 240 miles, so $a = 240$.

Since $\alpha = 0.5$, $1 - \alpha/2 = 0.75$, and hence the 0.75-quantile of $N(0, 1)$ is required. This is $z = 0.6745$. Using Formula (6.1) gives

$$b = \left(\frac{U - L}{2z}\right)^2 = \left(\frac{260 - 220}{2 \times 0.6745}\right)^2 \simeq 879.$$

Thus the assessed normal prior is $N(240, 879)$.

Solution 6.9

The assessed mode is 10, so $a = 10$.

The neuropsychologist assessed the quartiles of the prior for θ to be 5 and 15. Hence, using Formula (6.1) with $z = 0.6745$,

$$b = \left(\frac{15 - 5}{2 \times 0.6745}\right)^2 \simeq 55.$$

Thus the assessed normal prior is $N(10, 55)$.

Solution 6.10

(a) The mode of a Beta(a, b) distribution is given by Formula (5.3):

$$\text{mode} = \frac{a-1}{a+b-2}.$$

(i) If the mode is 0.2 and $a = 5$, then

$$0.2 = \frac{5-1}{5+b-2}.$$

Solving this for b gives $b = 17$.

(ii) If the mode is 0.2 and $b = 16$, then

$$0.2 = \frac{a-1}{a+16-2}.$$

Solving this for a gives $a = 4.75$.

(b) In part (a)(i), you found that if $a = 5$, then $b = 17$, and in part (a)(ii), you found that if $b = 16$, then $a = 4.75$. This gives two assessments of a and two assessments of b. There is no 'correct' prior to use in this situation. A reasonable compromise is to use the average of the two assessments for a, and the average of the two assessments for b:

$$a = \frac{4.75 + 5}{2} = 4.875, \quad b = \frac{16 + 17}{2} = 16.5.$$

The mode of Beta$(4.875, 16.5)$ is 0.2, the same as the estimated mode, so Beta$(4.875, 16.5)$ would seem a sensible prior to use.

Solution 8.1

(a) In Example 8.1, $n = 50$ and $x = 11$, so $n - x = 39$. The posterior distribution is Beta$(11 + a, 39 + b)$ which is therefore of the form Beta$(a + x, b + n - x)$.

(b) The posteriors are found using Formula (8.3). For priors Beta$(5, 7)$, Beta$(60, 90)$, Beta$(5, 2)$ and Beta$(110, 28)$, the posteriors are Beta$(16, 46)$, Beta$(71, 129)$, Beta$(16, 41)$ and Beta$(121, 67)$, respectively.

Solution 8.2

(a) The data are $n = 58$ and $x = 5$, so $n - x = 53$. Therefore using Formula (8.3), the posterior is

$$\text{Beta}(1.42 + 5, 5.13 + 53) = \text{Beta}(6.42, 58.13).$$

(b) Since $a + b = 1.42 + 5.13 = 6.55$ for the prior, and $n = 58$ for the data, the contribution of the data is far greater than that of the prior. Therefore the posterior will be closer to the likelihood than to the prior.

The prior, the likelihood and the posterior are shown in Figure S.8.

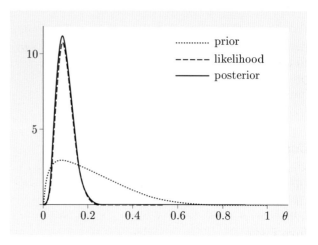

Figure S.8   Prior, likelihood and posterior for heart failure in babies

The figure confirms that the posterior is closer to the likelihood than to the prior.

Solution 8.3

(a) Data are given for 4 years, so $n = 4$. Also, $n\bar{x} = 2 + 1 + 3 + 1 = 7$. Therefore, using Formula (8.4), the posterior for θ is Gamma$(4.7 + 7, 4.8 + 4)$, that is, Gamma$(11.7, 8.8)$.

(b) In Figure 8.2, the posterior mode is roughly halfway between the prior mode and the likelihood mode. This suggests that the prior and the likelihood contribute roughly equally to the posterior.

Solution 8.4

For the data in Table 8.3,

$$\bar{x} = \frac{1}{12} \sum_{i=1}^{12} x_i = 7.5.$$

The posterior distribution is normal with mean and variance given by Formula (8.5):

$$\begin{aligned}
\text{mean} &= \frac{\sigma^2 a + nb\bar{x}}{\sigma^2 + nb} \\
&= \frac{90 \times 10 + 12 \times 55 \times 7.5}{90 + 12 \times 55} = 7.8,
\end{aligned}$$

$$\begin{aligned}
\text{variance} &= \frac{\sigma^2 b}{\sigma^2 + nb} \\
&= \frac{90 \times 55}{90 + 12 \times 55} = 6.6.
\end{aligned}$$

The posterior for θ is therefore $N(7.8, 6.6)$.

Solution 8.5

Since a $U(0, 1)$ prior is equivalent to a Beta$(1, 1)$ prior, the posterior can be found using Formula (8.3) with $a = 1$ and $b = 1$. This gives

$$\theta|\text{data} \sim \text{Beta}(1 + x, 1 + n - x),$$

as required.

Solution 8.6

(a) Using Formula (8.8), the posterior for μ, given the data, is normal with mean $\overline{x} = -36$ and variance $\sigma^2/n = 100/20 = 5$. So the posterior is $N(-36, 5)$.

(b) The two posterior distributions are rather similar, because the data contribute much more than the prior to the posterior in Example 8.4. Thus replacing the prior with one of ignorance (represented by the improper uniform prior) makes little difference to the results.

Solution 9.1

Since each distribution is normal, the mode is equal to the mean. Therefore the prior mode for θ is 10, and the posterior mode is 7.8. Thus the posterior mode is a little lower than the prior mode. This is also evident from Figure 9.1. Hence the data suggest that the most likely value for θ is lower than the neuropsychologist believed.

Solution 9.2

(a) The mode of a beta distribution is given by Formula (5.3). Hence the modes are 0.25 for $Beta(16, 46)$, 0.35 for $Beta(71, 129)$, 0.27 for $Beta(16, 41)$ and 0.65 for $Beta(121, 67)$.

(b) The location has been affected more when using the prior $Beta(5, 7)$ than when using the prior $Beta(60, 90)$. Similarly, the location has been affected more when using the prior $Beta(5, 2)$ than when using the prior $Beta(110, 28)$. In general, for two priors with the same mode, the location will be affected more by the data when using the weaker prior than when using the stronger prior.

Solution 9.3

The variance of $N(a, b)$ is b, so the posterior variance is 6.6. The prior variance was 55, so there is far less uncertainty about the value of θ after observing the data than there was before.

Solution 9.4

The posterior distribution is $N(7.8, 6.6)$, so

$$P(\theta > 0) = P\left(Z > \frac{0 - 7.8}{\sqrt{6.6}}\right), \quad \text{where } Z \sim N(0, 1),$$
$$\simeq P(Z > -3.04)$$
$$= P(Z < 3.04)$$
$$= 0.9988 \simeq 0.999.$$

Therefore after observing the data, you are almost certain that, on average, there is an improvement on the memory test for epilepsy patients who do not have surgery.

Solution 9.5

(a) The posterior is $N(7.8, 6.6)$, so

$$P(\theta \leq 2.76) = P\left(Z \leq \frac{2.76 - 7.8}{\sqrt{6.6}}\right)$$
$$\simeq P(Z \leq -1.96)$$

and

$$P(\theta \geq 12.84) = P\left(Z \geq \frac{12.84 - 7.8}{\sqrt{6.6}}\right)$$
$$\simeq P(Z \geq 1.96).$$

However, $P(Z \leq -1.96) = P(Z \geq 1.96)$, so $P(\theta \leq 2.76) = P(\theta > 12.84)$, and hence the credible interval $(2.76, 12.84)$ is an equal-tailed credible interval.

Since the posterior is normal, it is symmetric. Therefore the equal-tailed credible interval is also an HPD interval.

(b) Since the posterior is $N(7.8, 6.6)$, l is the 0.005-quantile and u is the 0.995-quantile of $N(7.8, 6.6)$.

The 0.995-quantile of $N(0, 1)$ is 2.576, so the 0.005-quantile is -2.576. Therefore the 0.005-quantile of $N(7.8, 6.6)$ is given by

$$l = 7.8 - 2.576 \times \sqrt{6.6} \simeq 1.18,$$

and the 0.995-quantile is given by

$$u = 7.8 + 2.576 \times \sqrt{6.6} \simeq 14.42.$$

Hence the 99% equal-tailed credible interval for θ is $(1.18, 14.42)$.

Solution 10.1

A beta prior is a natural choice for an unknown quantity defined on $(0, 1)$, so a reasonable choice is a $Beta(a, b)$ distribution. It can be shown that a beta prior with parameters $a = 2.9$ and $b = 8.6$ reflects the expert's beliefs quite satisfactorily. A uniform prior distribution would not be appropriate as the expert does not believe that all values of θ are equally likely.

Solution 11.1

(a) From the density histogram in Figure 11.1(b), it appears that the posterior distribution for θ_1 is roughly symmetric around a central value of about 0.5. Values of θ_1 greater than 0.8 or less than 0.2 appear very unlikely indeed, since none are generated in this sample.

(b) The main features of the $Beta(19, 19)$ distribution can be detected from the density histogram, but the smoothness of the p.d.f. is not well represented, since the histogram appears jagged. The density histogram is an adequate but somewhat rough-and-ready estimate of the true p.d.f. A better representation could be obtained by taking a much larger sample of simulated values.

Solution 11.2

The appropriate estimate of the posterior median of θ is the sample median. In general, distributional quantities are simply estimated by their sample equivalents.

Solution 11.3

(a) The estimated equal-tailed 95% credible interval indicates that there is a probability of 0.95 that the true proportion of urine samples correctly detected by dogs trained on fresh urine lies between 0.330 and 0.666. That is, it is highly likely that the true value is between these values.

(b) The estimated interval is not too dissimilar from the true interval. Since the estimated interval is a little wider than the true interval, inferences based on the estimate would be on the conservative side. The estimate could be improved upon by simulating a larger number of values from the $\text{Beta}(19, 19)$ distribution.

Solution 11.4

The ratio of the MC error to the sample standard deviation is

$$\frac{0.00269}{0.0850} \simeq 0.0316 < 0.05.$$

Hence, by the 5% rule of thumb, the sample size is adequate.

Solution 13.1

The value 1.06 is contained within the estimated equal-tailed 95% credible interval for ϕ given in Example 13.1. Furthermore, from Figure 13.2, the value 1.06 lies in a high density region of the posterior distribution, so there is very little evidence to suggest that the sex ratio in Milton Keynes is different from that in the European population as a whole.

Solution 13.2

The posterior distribution is unimodal, centred around 0.25 (approximately), and is slightly left-skew. The estimated equal-tailed 95% credible interval $(-0.007, 0.477)$ provides a range of plausible values for d since (approximately) 95% of the posterior probability is assigned to values in this range. This says that a value of $d = 0$, corresponding to no difference between the true proportions, is plausible, but perhaps unlikely. If a point estimate of d is required, then the posterior mean is appropriate. An estimate of the posterior mean is 0.2496 (0.0012). The simulation provides weak evidence that there is a difference between the two proportions, and that the proportion of urine samples that are correctly identified by dogs trained using fresh urine is greater than the corresponding proportion for dogs trained using dried urine.

Solution 14.1

Your answer will depend on your beliefs — there is no right or wrong answer. Many people's beliefs about μ would not be influenced by the value of τ, the precision of the model for Cavendish's measurements. That is, the accuracy of Cavendish's measuring equipment would have no effect on what values of μ they believed were likely. Their prior beliefs about μ and τ would be independent. Of course, for other people, dependence between μ and τ might seem appropriate.

Solution 14.2

Cavendish's measurements have been very informative about μ, the density of the Earth. The mean has increased from 4 to around 5.44, and the range of likely values is now much more concentrated around the mean value.

Solution 14.3

The points in the scatterplot of the simulated values from the posterior distribution form a triangular pattern: this shows that the variance of μ decreases as τ increases.

Solution 14.4

The accepted value of 5.515 is included in the estimated equal-tailed 95% credible interval, indicating that it is a plausible value. There are two likely reasons for any discrepancy between the true value and the posterior distribution: the quality of Cavendish's measurements, and the prior beliefs about μ that were incorporated into the analysis. A third, less likely, reason for any discrepancy is that the density of the Earth has changed since 1798.

Solution 16.1

Prior to the data being collected, the traffic expert believed that the most likely value of θ was 0.2, and that θ was unlikely to be greater than 0.6. The estimated posterior density indicates that the most likely value of θ is about 0.42, and that θ lies between 0.35 and 0.5 with high probability. Thus after observing the data, the most likely value of θ has increased and the uncertainty about θ has been reduced.

Solution 17.1

Any initial values which have high prior probability density could be used. For example, the prior mean (and mode) of μ and the prior mean of $\log \sigma$ seem as sensible as any other values: $\mu = 0$ and $\log \sigma = 0$.

Solution 17.2

This is clearly a situation where practical convergence is achieved only after many iterations. For both μ and $\log \sigma$, the three simulations start to overlap after about 1000 iterations. (In fact, a close-up of the first 1000 iterations shows that even by iteration 1000 the realizations of the Markov chain are not overlapping). A more conservative assessment of practical convergence would be that it has been reached after 2000 iterations. It is better to overestimate m than to underestimate it.

Solution 17.3

The posterior distribution for μ is concentrated on values between about 20 and 30. The probability of a negative catch is negligible despite the prior probability of 0.5. The weak prior does not appear to have significantly influenced the posterior inferences.

Solutions to Exercises

Solution 1.1

(a) The relative frequency can be used to estimate the probability, so an estimate is given by

$$\frac{\text{number of mothers who pack crisps every day}}{\text{number of mothers questioned}}$$

$$= \frac{374}{720} \simeq 0.52.$$

(b) Using the relative frequency, an estimate is given by

$$\frac{\text{number of children who bring crisps every day that week}}{\text{number of children in the class}}$$

$$= \frac{19}{28} \simeq 0.68.$$

(c) The estimate in part (a) is likely to be more reliable for two reasons. First, it is based on far more data. Secondly, since the estimate in part (b) is based on data from a single class, it may not be representative of the UK as a whole — for example, the children in the class may all be of a similar social background and this could affect the contents of their lunchboxes. (Also, some of the children in part (b) may have packed their own lunchboxes, whereas the implication in part (a) is that the lunchboxes were all packed by the mothers. The data may not be comparable.)

Solution 2.1

(a) (i) The test gives a positive result for all people infected with HIV, so

$$P(\text{positive result}|\text{person infected with HIV}) = 1.$$

(ii) The test gives a positive result for 0.005% of people not infected with HIV, so

$$P(\text{positive result}|\text{person not infected with HIV})$$
$$= \frac{0.005}{100} = 0.000\,05.$$

(b) (i) Since 10 in 100 000 women in this low-risk group are infected with HIV, the prior probability that the woman is infected is

$$P(\text{infected}) = \frac{10}{100\,000} = 0.0001.$$

(ii) The required probability can be calculated using Bayes' theorem. First, using Formula (2.3),

$$P(\text{infected}|\text{positive})$$
$$= \frac{P(\text{positive}|\text{infected}) \times P(\text{infected})}{P(\text{positive})}$$
$$= \frac{1 \times 0.0001}{P(\text{positive})}.$$

Now applying Formula (2.4) to find $P(\text{positive})$ gives

$$P(\text{positive})$$
$$= P(\text{positive}|\text{infected}) \times P(\text{infected})$$
$$\qquad + P(\text{positive}|\text{not infected}) \times P(\text{not infected})$$
$$= 1 \times 0.0001 + 0.000\,05 \times 0.9999$$
$$= 0.000\,149\,995.$$

Therefore

$$P(\text{infected}|\text{positive}) = \frac{1 \times 0.0001}{0.000\,149\,995} \simeq 0.667.$$

With a posterior probability of 0.667, it is far from certain that a woman in this low-risk group who has a positive test result is infected with HIV.

Solution 2.2

The posterior probability can be calculated using Bayes' theorem. First, using Formula (2.3),

$$P(\text{in square}|\text{not found})$$
$$= \frac{P(\text{not found}|\text{in square}) \times P(\text{in square})}{P(\text{not found})}$$
$$= \frac{(1 - 0.75) \times 0.4}{P(\text{not found})}$$
$$= \frac{0.1}{P(\text{not found})}.$$

Now applying Formula (2.4) to calculate $P(\text{not found})$ gives

$$P(\text{not found})$$
$$= P(\text{not found}|\text{in square}) \times P(\text{in square})$$
$$\qquad + P(\text{not found}|\text{not in square}) \times P(\text{not in square})$$
$$= 0.25 \times 0.4 + 1 \times 0.6$$
$$= 0.7.$$

Hence

$$P(\text{in square}|\text{not found}) = \frac{0.1}{0.7} \simeq 0.143.$$

Solution 2.3

(a) (i) If a female carrier has a son, then the probability that the son is affected by haemophilia is 0.5, so

$$P(\text{Jack is not affected}|\text{Kate is a carrier}) = 1 - 0.5$$
$$= 0.5.$$

(ii) If a female is not a carrier, then any son she may have will not be affected, so

$$P(\text{Jack is not affected}|\text{Kate is not a carrier}) = 1.$$

(b) Using Bayes' theorem (and abbreviating the names to J and K), Formula (2.3) gives

$P(\text{Kate is a carrier}|\text{Jack not affected})$

$= \dfrac{P(\text{J not affected}|\text{K carrier}) \times P(\text{K carrier})}{P(\text{J not affected})}$

$= \dfrac{0.5 \times 0.5}{P(\text{J not affected})}$

$= \dfrac{0.25}{P(\text{J not affected})}.$

Using Formula (2.4),

$P(\text{J not affected})$

$= P(\text{J not affected}|\text{K carrier}) \times P(\text{K carrier})$
$\quad + P(\text{J not affected}|\text{K not carrier})$
$\qquad \times P(\text{K not carrier})$

$= 0.5 \times 0.5 + 1 \times 0.5$

$= 0.75.$

Hence

$P(\text{Kate is a carrier}|\text{Jack not affected}) = \dfrac{0.25}{0.75} = \dfrac{1}{3}.$

(c) The new posterior probability is

$P(\text{Kate is a carrier}|\text{Jack and Luke are not affected}).$

This can be calculated using Bayes' theorem, as given in Formulas (2.7) and (2.8). Abbreviating the names to K, J and L, and using Formula (2.7), gives

$P(\text{K carrier}|\text{J and L not affected})$

$= P(\text{L not affected}|\text{K carrier, J not affected})$
$\quad \times P(\text{K carrier}|\text{J not affected})$
$\qquad / P(\text{L not affected}|\text{J not affected}).$

Since the probability that a carrier has a son who is affected is the same for each son, the probability that Luke is affected does not depend on whether or not Jack is affected. Therefore

$P(\text{L not affected}|\text{K carrier, J not affected})$

$= P(\text{L not affected}|\text{K carrier}) = 0.5.$

From part (b),

$P(\text{K carrier}|\text{J not affected}) = \tfrac{1}{3}.$

Hence

$P(\text{K carrier}|\text{J and L not affected})$

$= \dfrac{0.5 \times \tfrac{1}{3}}{P(\text{L not affected}|\text{J not affected})}.$

Now using Formula (2.8),

$P(\text{L not affected}|\text{J not affected})$

$= P(\text{L not affected}|\text{K carrier, J not affected})$
$\quad \times P(\text{K carrier}|\text{J not affected})$
$\quad + P(\text{L not affected}|\text{K not carrier, J not affected})$
$\quad \times P(\text{K not carrier}|\text{J not affected}).$

Now

$P(\text{L not affected}|\text{K not carrier, J not affected})$

$= P(\text{L not affected}|\text{K not carrier})$

$= 1,$

$P(\text{K not carrier}|\text{J not affected})$

$= 1 - P(\text{K carrier}|\text{J not affected})$

$= \tfrac{2}{3}.$

Hence

$P(\text{L not affected}|\text{J not affected})$

$= 0.5 \times \tfrac{1}{3} + 1 \times \tfrac{2}{3}$

$= \tfrac{5}{6}.$

Therefore the new posterior probability is

$\dfrac{0.5 \times \tfrac{1}{3}}{\tfrac{5}{6}} = 0.2.$

Solution 3.1

The posterior combines the information about θ contained in the prior with the information about θ contained in the likelihood.

In Figure 3.7(a), the prior and the likelihood are a similar height and width, so the prior and the likelihood are fairly similar in the strength of information they represent. Thus the posterior lies directly between the prior and the likelihood.

In Figure 3.7(b), the likelihood is strong in comparison to the prior. Therefore the posterior is closer to the likelihood than to the prior.

In Figure 3.7(c), the prior is strong in comparison to the likelihood. Consequently, the posterior is closer to the prior than to the likelihood.

Solution 5.1

(a) Since θ is a proportion, a beta prior may be suitable. A uniform prior $U(a, b)$ with $0 \le a < b \le 1$ may also be suitable.

(b) Since θ can take only positive values, a gamma prior may be suitable. If θ is expected to take only large values, then a normal prior might be adequate. An improper uniform prior $U(0, \infty)$ might also be suitable.

Solution 6.1

The interval $(185, 275)$ is not symmetric about the median 235. However, it is not too asymmetric, so a normal prior seems reasonable.

The assessed median is 235 miles, so a is estimated to be 235.

Lucy's assessed interval gives the quartiles for the prior. For $N(0, 1)$, $q_{0.75} = 0.6745$, so using Formula (6.1) with $z = 0.6745$, an estimate of b is given by

$$b = \left(\frac{U - L}{2z}\right)^2 = \left(\frac{275 - 185}{2 \times 0.6745}\right)^2 \simeq 4451.$$

Thus the normal prior is $N(235, 4451)$.

Notice that for this prior the lower quartile and the upper quartile are given by

$$q_{0.25} \simeq 235 - (0.6745 \times \sqrt{4451}) \simeq 190,$$

$$q_{0.75} \simeq 235 + (0.6745 \times \sqrt{4451}) \simeq 280.$$

These are not too far from Lucy's assessed quartiles of 185 and 275, so this approximation seems adequate.

Solution 6.2

(a) The mode of a Beta(a, b) distribution is given by Formula (5.3):

$$\text{mode} = \frac{a - 1}{a + b - 2}.$$

If $a = 10$ and the mode is 0.65, then

$$0.65 = \frac{10 - 1}{10 + b - 2}.$$

Solving this equation for b gives $b \simeq 5.85$.

(b) If $b = 10$ and the mode is 0.65, then

$$0.65 = \frac{a - 1}{a + 10 - 2}.$$

Solving this for a gives $a \simeq 17.7$.

(c) The prior in part (b) represents the stronger beliefs about θ because both a and b (and hence $a + b$) are larger for this prior.

Solution 6.3

(a) The mode of a Gamma(a, b) distribution is given by Formula (5.5):

$$\text{mode} = \frac{a - 1}{b}.$$

If $a = 7$ and the mode is 4, then

$$4 = \frac{7 - 1}{b},$$

which gives $b = 1.5$.

(b) If $b = 2$ and the mode is 4, then

$$4 = \frac{a - 1}{2},$$

which gives $a = 9$.

(c) In part (a), you found that if $a = 7$ then $b = 1.5$. In part (b), you found that if $b = 2$ then $a = 9$. Therefore you have two assessments of a and two assessments of b. There is no 'correct' prior to use in this situation. You could try using the average of the assessments for a and the average of the assessments for b:

$$a = \frac{7 + 9}{2} = 8, \quad b = \frac{1.5 + 2}{2} = 1.75.$$

The mode of Gamma$(8, 1.75)$ is 4, the same as the assessed mode, so Gamma$(8, 1.75)$ would seem a sensible prior to use.

Solution 8.1

For the beta/binomial model, the posterior distribution is given by (8.3):

$$\theta | \text{data} \sim \text{Beta}(a + x, b + n - x).$$

(a) In this case, $a = 2$, $b = 6$, $x = 5$ and $n = 58$, so the posterior is Beta$(7, 59)$.

(b) For $a = 20$, $b = 60$, $x = 5$ and $n = 58$, the posterior is Beta$(25, 113)$.

(c) In part (a), $a + b = 8$, which is much smaller than $n = 58$, so the contribution of the data is much greater than that of the prior. In part (b), $a + b = 80$, which is substantially greater than $n = 58$. Hence in this case, the contribution of the prior is greater than that of the data.

Solution 8.2

(a) When the prior is Gamma(a, b), the posterior distribution is given by (8.4):

$$\theta | \text{data} \sim \text{Gamma}(a + n\overline{x}, b + n).$$

For $a = 4$, $b = 6$, $\overline{x} = 7/4$ and $n = 4$, the posterior is Gamma$(11, 10)$.

(b) With an improper uniform prior, the posterior distribution is given by (8.7):

$$\theta | \text{data} \sim \text{Gamma}(n\overline{x}, n).$$

Since $\overline{x} = 7/4$ and $n = 4$, the posterior is Gamma$(7, 4)$.

Solution 9.1

The priors Beta$(5, 7)$ and Beta$(5, 2)$ represent weak prior beliefs about θ. Thus the data will be very informative about θ in comparison to these weak priors. Since the posterior combines the two sources of information — the prior and the data — the posterior uncertainty regarding θ will be less than the prior uncertainty.

On the other hand, the prior Beta$(60, 90)$ represents far stronger prior beliefs about θ. Therefore the data will not be quite so informative in comparison to the prior. When combining the information from the prior with the information from the data, the uncertainty regarding θ will not be reduced by quite so much.

The prior Beta$(110, 28)$ is a strong prior with mode 0.8. The observed proportion, 0.22, was not expected under this prior, so the data conflict with the prior. Thus the data do not reduce the uncertainty about θ; in fact, they increase it slightly.

Solution 9.2

The posterior is $N(35, 38.1)$. For a 95% equal-tailed credible interval, l is the 0.025-quantile and u is the 0.975-quantile of the posterior distribution.

The 0.975-quantile of $N(0, 1)$ is 1.96, so the 0.025-quantile is -1.96. Therefore

$$l = 35 - 1.96 \times \sqrt{38.1} \simeq 22.9,$$
$$u = 35 + 1.96 \times \sqrt{38.1} \simeq 47.1.$$

So the 95% equal-tailed credible interval is $(22.9, 47.1)$.

As the posterior distribution is symmetric, the HPD interval is the same as the equal-tailed credible interval. So the 95% HPD interval will not be shorter than the 95% equal-tailed credible interval.

Solution 9.3

(a) The HPD credible interval is (a, c).

(b) The equal-tailed interval is (b, d).

Solution 11.1

(a) Although increasing N, the number of values simulated, reduces the MC error, it does not reduce the posterior uncertainty about θ. The intervals calculated from the two simulations are estimates of the same credible interval, so there is no reason why the width of the interval estimated using the larger sample should be less than the width of the interval estimated using the smaller sample. However, the larger sample will provide a *better* estimate of the width.

(b) Increasing the amount of data tenfold will reduce the posterior uncertainty about θ, so the equal-tailed 95% posterior credible interval will be narrower. Therefore its estimate, based on $N = 10\,000$ simulated values, is likely to be less than 2.12.

Solution 11.2

The MC error, as a proportion of the sample standard deviation, is
$$\frac{0.0234}{0.2632} \simeq 0.0889 > 0.05.$$
Hence, by the 5% rule of thumb, the number of values simulated is not adequate, and should be increased.

Solution 13.1

(a) Since $\sigma = 1/\sqrt{\tau}$, the transformation $1/\sqrt{\tau}$ should be applied to the simulated values of τ. The transformed values will be a sample from the posterior distribution for σ, and thus can be used to make inferences about σ in the usual way.

(b) Since the first simulated value of τ is 0.0057, the first simulated value of σ is $1/\sqrt{0.0057} \simeq 13.245$. The next four simulated values are obtained in the same way. Thus the first five simulated values (to three decimal places) are 13.245, 14.142, 14.434, 16.013, 19.245.

Solution 14.1

(a) From the density histogram, the posterior mode of τ lies between 15 and 20; a reasonable estimate is 17.5.

(b) Using Formula (5.5) for the mode of a gamma distribution, the mode of Gamma$(16.7, 0.982)$ is
$$\text{mode} = \frac{16.7 - 1}{0.982} \simeq 16.0.$$
This value is not too dissimilar from the estimate obtained in part (a).

Solution 17.1

A prior which satisfies the requirement that μ should be non-negative is a gamma prior:
$$\mu \sim \text{Gamma}(a, b).$$
The mean of Gamma(a, b) is a/b, and the variance is a/b^2. When $a = 1$ and $b = 0.1$, the gamma prior has mean 10 and variance 100. (Other values of a and b such that $a/b^2 = 100$ would also be appropriate.)

This model does not result in a conjugate analysis. However, MCMC could be used to estimate the posterior distribution.

Solution 17.2

The trace plots do not start to overlap until around iteration 2000. Before that iteration, convergence cannot be deemed to have been reached. In other words, the burn-in period must extend to at least iteration 2000. Choosing a burn-in of 3000 seems to be a sensible, if somewhat conservative, choice.

Solution 20.1

This exercise covers some of the ideas and techniques discussed in Section 2.

(a) Since 0.1% of women aged between 40 and 49 who are screened have breast cancer, and all that is known about both Emma and Helen is that they are in this age range, an estimate of the prior probability of having breast cancer is 0.001 for both women.

(b) Let
$$D = \text{abnormality detected from mammogram.}$$
From the information given,
$$P(D|\text{cancer}) = 0.87,$$
$$P(D|\text{not cancer}) = 0.05.$$
From part (a), $P(\text{cancer}) = 0.001$.

The probability required is $P(\text{cancer}|D)$, and this can be found using Bayes' theorem, as follows. Using (2.3) gives
$$P(\text{cancer}|D) = \frac{P(D|\text{cancer})P(\text{cancer})}{P(D)},$$
where $P(D)$ is obtained using (2.4). Thus $P(D)$ is given by
$$P(D|\text{cancer})P(\text{cancer}) + P(D|\text{not cancer})P(\text{not cancer})$$
$$= 0.87 \times 0.001 + 0.05 \times (1 - 0.001)$$
$$= 0.050\,82.$$
Hence
$$P(\text{cancer}|D) = \frac{0.87 \times 0.001}{0.050\,82} \simeq 0.017.$$

The posterior probability that Emma has breast cancer after detecting an abnormality in her mammogram is 0.017, which is greater than the prior probability of 0.001. However, the posterior probability is still small, and despite an abnormality having been detected, it is far more likely that she does not have breast cancer:
$$P(\text{not cancer}|D) = 1 - P(\text{cancer}|D) = 0.983.$$

(c) There is no abnormality detected with Helen's mammogram, and
$$P(\text{not } D|\text{cancer}) = 1 - P(D|\text{cancer}) = 0.13.$$
The probability required is $P(\text{cancer}|\text{not } D)$. This can be found using Bayes' theorem. Using (2.3) gives
$$P(\text{cancer}|\text{not } D) = \frac{P(\text{not } D|\text{cancer})P(\text{cancer})}{P(\text{not } D)}$$
$$= \frac{0.13 \times 0.001}{1 - 0.050\,82}$$
$$\simeq 0.000\,14.$$

The posterior probability that Helen has breast cancer after no abnormalities have been detected in her mammogram is 0.000\,14, which is less than the prior probability of 0.001.

Solution 20.2

This exercise covers some of the ideas and techniques discussed in Sections 2 and 3.

(a) $P(X = 8|\theta = 0.03) = L(0.03)$, and similarly for the other terms. So, using the likelihood and prior probability values given in the question,

$$
\begin{aligned}
P(X = 8) &= P(X = 8|\theta = 0.03)P(\theta = 0.03) \\
&\quad + P(X = 8|\theta = 0.04)P(\theta = 0.04) \\
&\quad + P(X = 8|\theta = 0.05)P(\theta = 0.05) \\
&\quad + P(X = 8|\theta = 0.06)P(\theta = 0.06) \\
&= 0.040 \times \tfrac{1}{2} + 0.097 \times \tfrac{1}{6} \\
&\quad + 0.138 \times \tfrac{1}{6} + 0.139 \times \tfrac{1}{6} \\
&\simeq 0.0823.
\end{aligned}
$$

(b) To obtain the posterior distribution for θ, the posterior probability for each of the four possible values for θ must be calculated using Formula (2.3) as follows:

$$
\begin{aligned}
P(\theta = 0.03|X = 8) &= \frac{P(X = 8|\theta = 0.03)P(\theta = 0.03)}{P(X = 8)} \\
&\simeq \frac{0.040 \times \tfrac{1}{2}}{0.0823} \\
&\simeq 0.243,
\end{aligned}
$$

$$
\begin{aligned}
P(\theta = 0.04|X = 8) &= \frac{P(X = 8|\theta = 0.04)P(\theta = 0.04)}{P(X = 8)} \\
&\simeq \frac{0.097 \times \tfrac{1}{6}}{0.0823} \\
&\simeq 0.196,
\end{aligned}
$$

$$
\begin{aligned}
P(\theta = 0.05|X = 8) &= \frac{P(X = 8|\theta = 0.05)P(\theta = 0.05)}{P(X = 8)} \\
&\simeq \frac{0.138 \times \tfrac{1}{6}}{0.0823} \\
&\simeq 0.279,
\end{aligned}
$$

$$
\begin{aligned}
P(\theta = 0.06|X = 8) &= \frac{P(X = 8|\theta = 0.06)P(\theta = 0.06)}{P(X = 8)} \\
&\simeq \frac{0.139 \times \tfrac{1}{6}}{0.0823} \\
&\simeq 0.281.
\end{aligned}
$$

(c) Observing $X = 8$ has changed the prior beliefs quite dramatically. The posterior probabilities for $\theta = 0.05$ and $\theta = 0.06$ are the largest. The most likely value is $\theta = 0.06$.

(d) The posterior probability that the cancer rate is the same nationally as at Slater School is $P(\theta = 0.03|X = 8) \simeq 0.243$. Thus the posterior probability that the cancer rate is higher at Slater School than nationally is $P(\theta > 0.03|X = 8) \simeq 0.757$. This suggests that the cancer rate is higher at Slater School than nationally.

Solution 20.3

This exercise covers some of the ideas and techniques discussed in Section 5.

(a) The mode of Beta(a, b) is given by Formula (5.3):
$$
\text{mode} = \frac{a - 1}{a + b - 2}.
$$
For Beta$(6, 4)$,
$$
\text{mode} = \frac{6 - 1}{6 + 4 - 2} = 0.625,
$$
and for Beta$(31, 19)$,
$$
\text{mode} = \frac{31 - 1}{31 + 19 - 2} = 0.625,
$$
so the modes are the same.

(b) The mode of Gamma(a, b) is given by Formula (5.5):
$$
\text{mode} = \frac{a - 1}{b}.
$$
For Gamma$(11, 2)$,
$$
\text{mode} = \frac{11 - 1}{2} = 5,
$$
and for Gamma$(1.5, 0.1)$,
$$
\text{mode} = \frac{1.5 - 1}{0.1} = 5,
$$
so the modes are the same.

(c) The mode of $N(a, b)$ is a. Therefore both normal priors have mode 10.

Solution 20.4

This exercise covers some of the ideas and techniques discussed in Sections 3 and 5.

(a) For the beta prior Beta(a, b), the larger the value of $a + b$ is, the stronger is the prior. Therefore Beta$(40, 40)$ is the stronger prior.

(b) Since $a + b = 17$ for each prior, the priors are equally strong.

(c) For a normal prior, the value of the variance b dictates the strength of the prior: the smaller the variance is, the stronger is the prior. So $N(10, 4)$ is the stronger prior.

Solution 20.5

This exercise covers some of the ideas and techniques discussed in Sections 5 and 8.

(a) Since ϕ is a probability, it lies between 0 and 1, so a beta prior is a natural prior to use for ϕ.

(b) The mode of Beta(a, b) is given by Formula (5.3), so for Beta$(42.5, 7.5)$,
$$
\text{mode} = \frac{42.5 - 1}{42.5 + 7.5 - 2} \simeq 0.86.
$$
The variance of Beta(a, b) is given by
$$
\text{variance} = \frac{a \times b}{(a + b)^2(a + b + 1)}.
$$
Therefore the variance of Beta$(42.5, 7.5)$ is given by
$$
\text{variance} = \frac{42.5 \times 7.5}{(42.5 + 7.5)^2(42.5 + 7.5 + 1)} = 0.0025,
$$
and the standard deviation is 0.05.

(c) Using Formula (8.3), the posterior distribution for ϕ is

$$\phi | \text{data} \sim \text{Beta}(42.5 + 23, 7.5 + 50 - 23)$$
$$= \text{Beta}(65.5, 34.5).$$

(d) For the posterior Beta(65.5, 34.5),

$$\text{mode} = \frac{65.5 - 1}{65.5 + 34.5 - 2} \simeq 0.66,$$

$$\text{variance} = \frac{65.5 \times 34.5}{(65.5 + 34.5)^2 (65.5 + 34.5 + 1)} \simeq 0.0022.$$

Therefore the posterior standard deviation is $\sqrt{0.0022} \simeq 0.047$.

(e) The data are in conflict with the prior beliefs about ϕ: before observing any data, ϕ was believed to be much larger than the data suggest. In fact, the prior mode is 0.86, while the observed proportion is only $23/50 = 0.46$. Furthermore, values of ϕ as low as 0.46 were not really thought possible under the prior.

As the data were not as expected, the posterior does not reflect much more confidence about the value of ϕ than the prior. This is reflected in the fact that the posterior standard deviation (0.047) is very similar to the prior standard deviation (0.05).

The prior has $a + b = 50$. Since n is also equal to 50, the prior and the likelihood contribute equally to the posterior. This explains why the posterior is mid-way between the prior and the likelihood.

Solution 20.6

This exercise covers some of the ideas and techniques discussed in Sections 6 and 8.

(a) The most likely value for θ is the mode, which is assessed to be -30. Therefore the assessed value for a is -30.

Using Formula (6.1), parameter b is given by

$$b = \left(\frac{U - L}{2 \times 0.6745} \right)^2 = \left(\frac{-25 - (-33)}{2 \times 0.6745} \right)^2 \simeq 35.2.$$

Therefore the normal prior which matches the assessed values is $N(-30, 35.2)$.

(b) Using Formula (8.5), the researcher's posterior is normal with mean and variance given by

$$\text{mean} = \frac{\sigma^2 a + nb\overline{x}}{\sigma^2 + nb}$$
$$= \frac{100 \times (-30) + 20 \times 35.2 \times (-36)}{100 + 20 \times 35.2}$$
$$\simeq -35.25,$$

$$\text{variance} = \frac{\sigma^2 b}{\sigma^2 + nb}$$
$$= \frac{100 \times 35.2}{100 + 20 \times 35.2}$$
$$\simeq 4.378.$$

(c) Since the normal distribution is symmetric, the HPD interval (l, u) is the same as the equal-tailed interval. The 0.975-quantile of $N(0, 1)$ is 1.96, so the 0.025-quantile is -1.96. Therefore

$$l \simeq -35.25 - 1.96 \times \sqrt{4.378} \simeq -39.35,$$
$$u \simeq -35.25 + 1.96 \times \sqrt{4.378} \simeq -31.15.$$

Therefore the 95% HPD interval for θ is $(-39.35, -31.15)$.

Solution 20.7

This exercise covers some of the ideas and techniques discussed in Sections 11 and 14, applied in the context of MCMC.

(a) As the value of τ increases, the variability of μ decreases. Thus the posterior distributions for μ and τ are not independent.

(b) (i) For each of μ and τ, the ratio of the MC error to the estimated standard deviation is less than 0.05. Hence, by the 5% rule of thumb, sufficient values were sampled.

(ii) For Gamma(a, b), the mean and variance are a/b and a/b^2, respectively. Therefore the priors for the parameters μ and τ have mean 10 and variance 100, and hence standard deviation 10. Since the posterior means and standard deviations are very different from the prior means and standard deviations, the data play the major role in determining the posterior values. This occurs because the priors have large variances, and are therefore weak priors.

Index